APPLYING KNOWLEDGE AND

Higher HUMAN BIOLOGY

for CfE

Writing Team:

James Torrance

James Fullarton

Clare Marsh

James Simms

Caroline Stevenson

Diagrams by **James Torrance**

HODDER GIBSON
AN HACHETTE UK COMPANY

D0351555

Biblio

The Publishers would like to thank the following for permission to reproduce copyright material:

Photo credits

p.l (background) and Unit 1 running head image © Alexandr Mitiuc – Fotolia.com, (inset left) © STEVE GSCHMEISSNER/SCIENCE PHOTO LIBRARY, (inset centre) © 3D4MEDICAL.COM/SCIENCE PHOTO LIBRARY, (inset right) © Michael J. Gregory, Ph.D./Clinton Community College; p.29 (background) and Unit 2 running head image © Imagestate Media (John Foxx), (inset left) © Dan Marschka/AP/Press Association Images, (inset centre) © DR NAJEEB LAYYOUS/SCIENCE PHOTO LIBRARY, (inset right) © DR P. MARAZZI/SCIENCE PHOTO LIBRARY; p.49 (background) and Unit 3 running head image © Sebastian Kaulitzki – Fotolia.com, (inset left) © DR P. MARAZZI/SCIENCE PHOTO LIBRARY, (inset centre) © STEVE GSCHMEISSNER/SCIENCE PHOTO LIBRARY, (inset right) © MEDICAL BODY SCANS/JESSICA WILSON/SCIENCE PHOTO LIBRARY; p.69 (background) and Unit 4 running head image © Sebastian Kaulitzki – Fotolia.com, (inset left) © DAVID SCHARF/SCIENCE PHOTO LIBRARY, (inset centre) © DAVID SCHARF/SCIENCE PHOTO LIBRARY, (inset right) © JOHN BAVOSI/SCIENCE PHOTO LIBRARY.

Acknowledgements

The authors and publisher would like to extend grateful thanks to Jim Stafford for assistance offered at manuscript stage of this book, as well as for further guidance and editorial advice during the production process.

Every effort has been made to trace all copyright holders, but if any have been inadvertently overlooked the Publishers will be pleased to make the necessary arrangements at the first opportunity.

Hachette UK's policy is to use papers that are natural, renewable and recyclable products and made from wood grown in sustainable forests. The logging and manufacturing processes are expected to conform to the environmental regulations of the country of origin.

Orders: please contact Bookpoint Ltd, 130 Milton Park, Abingdon, Oxon OX14 4SB. Telephone: (+44) 01235 827720. Fax: (+44) 01235 400454. Lines are open 9.00–5.00, Monday to Saturday, with a 24-hour message answering service. Visit our website at www.hoddereducation.co.uk. Hodder Gibson can be contacted direct on: Tel: 0141 848 1609; Fax: 0141 889 6315; email: hoddergibson@hodder.co.uk

© James Torrance, James Fullarton, Clare Marsh, James Simms, Caroline Stevenson 2013
First published in 2013 by
Hodder Gibson, an imprint of Hodder Education,
An Hachette UK Company
2a Christie Street
Paisley PA1 1NB

Impression number   5 4 3 2
Year   2016 2015
ISBN: 978 1444 192063

Cover photo © V. Yakobchuk – Fotolia.com
Illustrations by James Torrance
Typeset in Minion Pro 11pt by Fakenham Prepress Solutions, Fakenham, Norfolk NR21 8NN
Printed in Dubai

A catalogue record for this title is available from the British Library

Contents

The book you are holding is from the second (or subsequent) printing of this title. In this version the Chapter/Section names and page numbers have been amended from the first printing. These changes have been made in line with amendments that were made to the ordering of the Higher syllabus in summer 2014.

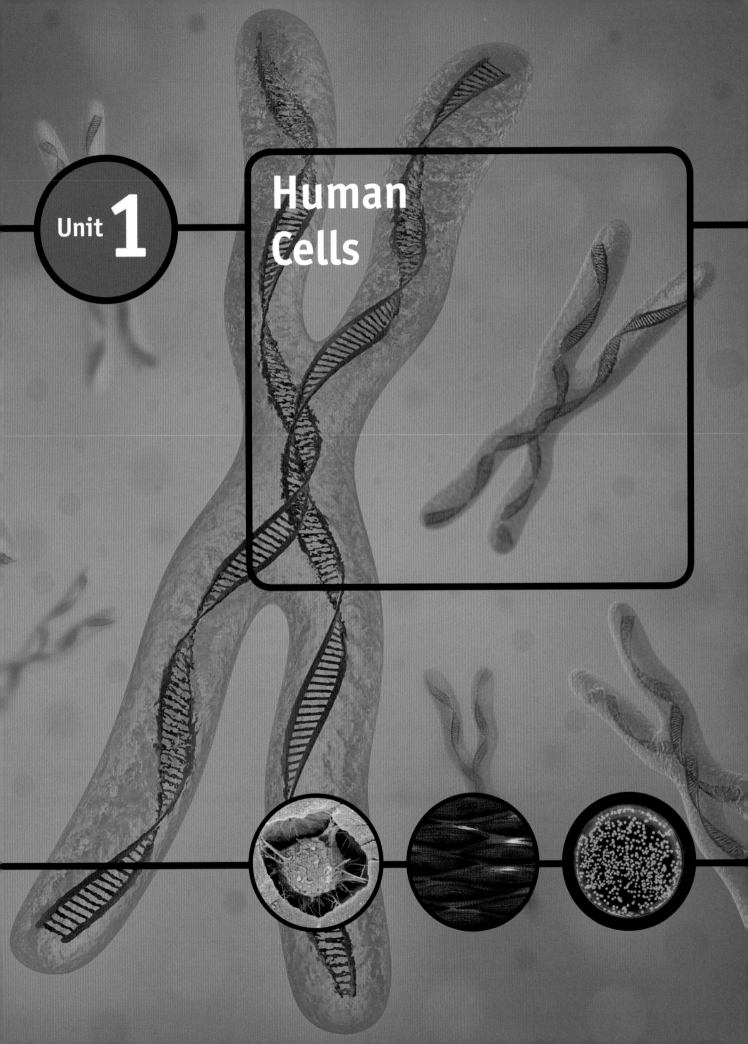

Unit 1

Human Cells

1 Division and differentiation in human cells

1 Figure 1.1 represents the processes of cell division and cellular differentiation in an animal.

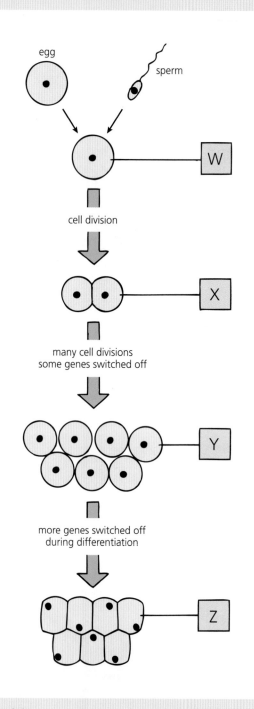

Figure 1.1

Match W, X, Y and Z with the following terms: *specialised cell, zygote, tissue (adult) stem cell* and *embryonic stem cell*. (3)

2 Read the passage and answer the questions that follow it.

Evidence from research strongly supports the theory that the type of white blood cell that a stem cell in red bone marrow becomes is determined by the sequence of differentiation signals that it receives. A stem cell has receptors on the surface of its membrane for several different signal proteins (SPs). Early in its development a stem cell has the potential to follow more than one differentiation pathway depending on which SP it first encounters.

Suppose that SP1 induces a stem cell to become a lymphocyte progenitor whereas SP2 induces it to become a phagocyte progenitor. If a stem cell has receptors for both SP1 and SP2 and happens to meet SP1 first, then this will stimulate the cell to divide into two cells that have lost the ability (switched off the gene) to make SP2 receptors but have switched on the genes for receptors for SPs 3, 4 and 5.

Suppose that SP3 induces a lymphocyte progenitor to become a natural killer cell, SP4 induces it to become a B lymphocyte and SP5 induces it to become a T lymphocyte. Then if the lymphocyte progenitor happens to meet SP3 first it will divide into natural killer cells that have lost their ability to make receptors for SPs 4 and 5. These genes are switched off and the cells cannot become B or T cells.

It is thought that, similarly, a phagocyte progenitor has receptors for SPs 6 and 7 where an encounter first with SP6 would induce it to become monocytes whereas a first meeting with SP7 would make it become phagocytes with a lobed nucleus.

a) What word in the passage means *a forerunner to a fully differentiated cell*? (1)

b) i) A stem cell was exposed to signal proteins (SPs) in the order 1, 4. Which type of white blood cell resulted?

ii) A second stem cell was exposed to SPs in the order 2, 6. Which type of white blood cell resulted? (2)

c) In order to differentiate into T lymphocytes, which SPs, and in which order, would a stem cell need to meet? (1)

d) A stem cell from red bone marrow was exposed to SP3 and then to SP1 but it failed to differentiate completely. Suggest why. (2)

3 The procedure that was adopted to produce 'Dolly the sheep' is shown in Figure 1.2.

a) What name is given to the technique employed to create the original cell that gave rise to Dolly? (1)

b) Why is Dolly said to be the result of a *cloning* procedure? (1)

c) i) Did Dolly develop a black face or a white face?
   ii) Explain your answer. (2)

d) i) What was the chance of Dolly being a ram?
      A 0   **B** 1 in 1   **C** 1 in 2
   ii) Explain your choice of answer. (2)

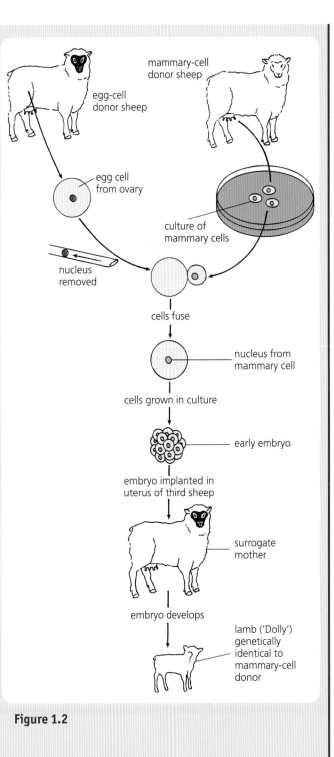

Figure 1.2

4 The ten statements shown in Figure 1. 3 were made by people interviewed about the use of human embryos for stem cell research.

a) Classify the statements into two groups:
   i) those in favour of this type of research
   ii) those opposed to this type of research. (2)
b) What would your position have been in this ethical debate if you had been interviewed?

5 The four people shown in Figure 1.4 all support the use of human embryos in stem cell research.

a) Who is making a statement based on fact rather than expressing an opinion? (1)
b) i) Do you consider this person's statement to be a convincing or an unconvincing argument in support of the use of embryonic stem cells for research?
   ii) Justify your answer. (2)

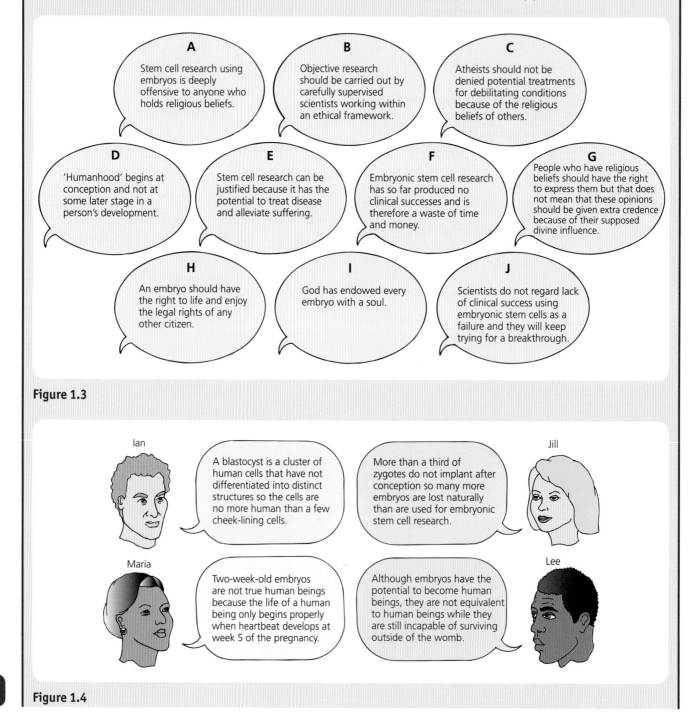

A Stem cell research using embryos is deeply offensive to anyone who holds religious beliefs.

B Objective research should be carried out by carefully supervised scientists working within an ethical framework.

C Atheists should not be denied potential treatments for debilitating conditions because of the religious beliefs of others.

D 'Humanhood' begins at conception and not at some later stage in a person's development.

E Stem cell research can be justified because it has the potential to treat disease and alleviate suffering.

F Embryonic stem cell research has so far produced no clinical successes and is therefore a waste of time and money.

G People who have religious beliefs should have the right to express them but that does not mean that these opinions should be given extra credence because of their supposed divine influence.

H An embryo should have the right to life and enjoy the legal rights of any other citizen.

I God has endowed every embryo with a soul.

J Scientists do not regard lack of clinical success using embryonic stem cells as a failure and they will keep trying for a breakthrough.

Figure 1.3

Ian: A blastocyst is a cluster of human cells that have not differentiated into distinct structures so the cells are no more human than a few cheek-lining cells.

Jill: More than a third of zygotes do not implant after conception so many more embryos are lost naturally than are used for embryonic stem cell research.

Maria: Two-week-old embryos are not true human beings because the life of a human being only begins properly when heartbeat develops at week 5 of the pregnancy.

Lee: Although embryos have the potential to become human beings, they are not equivalent to human beings while they are still incapable of surviving outside of the womb.

4

Figure 1.4

6 Table 1.1 refers to a country's lung cancer death rates.

	Lung cancer deaths per 100 000 population									
Year	2000	2001	2002	2003	2004	2005	2006	2007	2008	2009
Region A	51.2	48.3	52.8	49.3	47.7	47.5	48.4	47.4	47.4	47.2
Region B	60.1	57.8	61.1	60.2	62.5	57.7	53.6	53.6	52.3	51.4
Whole country	55.3	55.1	55.6	54.8	53.9	53.1	52.8	52.3	52.3	52.0

Table 1.1

a) By how many deaths per 100 000 was the lung cancer death rate for region B greater than that for region A in i) 2002? ii) 2007? (2)

b) i) How many people per million died of lung cancer in region A during 2004?
   ii) What percentage of people in the whole country died of lung cancer in 2009? (2)

c) i) Which region's data reflect more closely the trend shown by the country as a whole? Explain how you arrived at your answer.
   ii) In what way does the **overall** trend for the other region differ from that of the country as a whole? (3)

7 The data in Table 1.2 show the results of a survey carried out on people aged 45–64 years in a northern European country who died of melanoma skin cancer.

a) Draw a line graph of the data for the northern European country. (3)

b) Identify the **dependent** and the **independent** variables from your graph. (1)

c) What overall trend does the graph show? (1)

d) i) Which reading in the table is most likely to be a source of error?

ii) Justify your answer with reference to the data in the table. (3)

e) How many northern European people of this age group per million died of melanoma cancer in 1998? (1)

f) i) Calculate the percentage increase in deaths per 100 000 for the northern European country between 1990 and 1992.
   ii) Calculate the percentage decrease in deaths per 100 000 for all Europe between 1996 and 1997. (2)

g) i) Which of the following would be the most likely value of deaths per 100 000 for the northern European country for the year 2000?
   A 7.8   B 5.2   C 1.9
   ii) Explain your choice of answer. (2)

h) Suggest TWO reasons why death due to melanoma cancer is now less common among the people of this northern European country than it was in the 1990s. (2)

8 Give an account of the two types of stem cell and their research and therapeutic value. (9)

Year	Deaths per 100 000 population (northern European country)	Deaths per 100 000 population (all Europe)
1990	3.2	1.5
1991	3.7	1.9
1992	4.4	2.3
1993	3.6	1.8
1994	7.2	2.2
1995	4.7	2.2
1996	5.3	2.5
1997	4.9	2.3
1998	5.5	2.6
1999	5.5	2.7

Table 1.2

2 Structure and replication of DNA

1 Table 2.1 shows a sample of Chargaff's data following the analysis of DNA extracted from several species.

Species	%A	%C	%G	%T	A/T	G/C
Chicken	28.0	21.6	**Box X**	28.4	0.99	1.02
Grasshopper	29.3	20.7	20.7	29.3	1.00	1.00
Human	29.3	20.0	20.7	30.0	0.98	1.04
Maize	26.8	23.2	22.8	27.2	0.99	**Box Y**
Wheat	27.3	22.8	22.7	27.2	1.00	1.00

Table 2.1

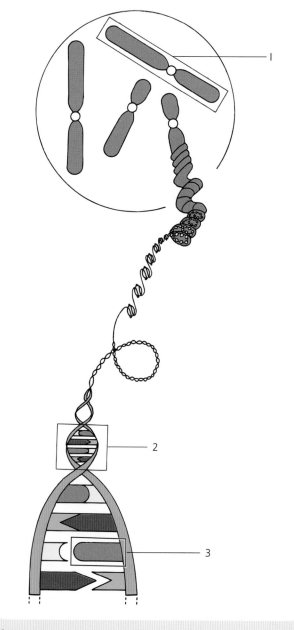

a) Study the data and calculate the figures that should have been entered in boxes X and Y. (2)

b) i) State Chargaff's rules (see core text page 22 for help).
   ii) Do the data in the table support these rules?
   iii) Explain your answer. (3)

c) With respect to the number of the different bases in a DNA sample, which of the following is correct? (1)
   A C = T   B A = G   C A+G = C+T   D A+T = G+C

2 a) Calculate the percentage of thymine bases present in a DNA molecule containing 1000 bases of which 200 are guanine. (1)

   b) State the number of cytosine bases present in a DNA molecule that contains 10 000 base molecules of which 18% are adenine. (1)

3 Figure 2.1 shows a cell's genetic material.

   a) i) Name the parts enclosed in boxes 1, 2 and 3.
      ii) Which of these boxed structures contains nucleic acid and consists of many different genes?
      iii) Which of these structures is one of four basic units whose order determines the information held in a gene? (5)

   b) The DNA helix of one of these chromosomes is found to be 5 cm long when fully uncoiled and 5 μm long when tightly coiled.
      i) Express these data as a packing ratio of fully extended DNA:tightly coiled DNA.
      ii) Suggest why scientists normally express the length of a chromosome in number of base pairs. (2)

4 When DNA is heated to 80°C, its component strands separate from one another. If the DNA is then cooled slowly, the strands become reunited as a double helix.

Figure 2.1

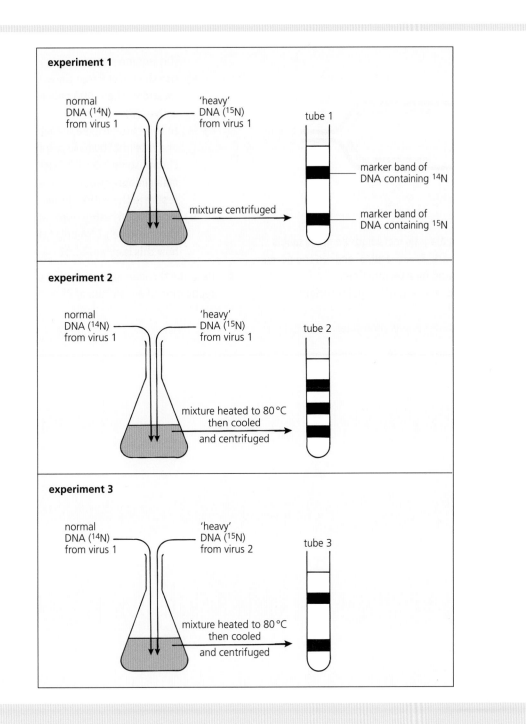

Figure 2.2

Figure 2.2 shows a series of experiments involving the use of DNA labelled with the common isotope of nitrogen (^{14}N) and DNA labelled with the heavy isotope of nitrogen (^{15}N).

a) Explain the results obtained in tube 2. (2)
b) Explain why tube 3 has only two bands. (2)
c) By what means could scientists produce a strain of bacteriophage virus with ^{15}N in its DNA? (3)

5 Figure 2.3 shows a replication 'bubble' on a strand of DNA.

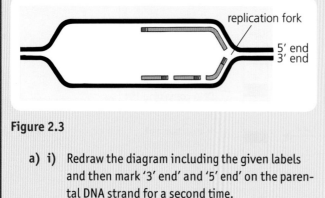

replication fork

5' end
3' end

Figure 2.3

a) i) Redraw the diagram including the given labels and then mark '3' end' and '5' end' on the parental DNA strand for a second time.
   ii) Draw in and label a starting point (origin of replication).
   iii) Label one of the primer molecules.
   iv) Label the leading DNA strand and a fragment of the lagging strand.
   v) Use the letter P four times to indicate all the locations where DNA polymerase would be active. (6)

b) i) In this chromosome the replication fork moves at a rate of 2500 base pairs per minute. If this chromosome is 5×10^7 base pairs in length, how many minutes would one replication fork take to replicate the entire chromosome?
   ii) However, in reality, replication of this chromosome's DNA only takes 3 minutes. Explain how this is achieved. (2)

6 Describe the main processes that occur during the replication of a molecule of DNA. (9)

3 Gene expression

1   Figure 3.1 shows a flow chart that refers to the coding for, and synthesis of, an active protein. Match the numbered arrows with the following answers. (3)

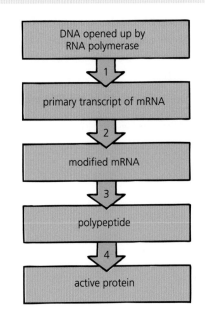

Figure 3.1

   a) cutting and splicing of primary transcript of mRNA
   b) post-translational modification
   c) transcription
   d) translation

2   Figure 3.2 shows the method by which the genetic code is transmitted during protein synthesis. Table 3.1 gives some of the triplets that correspond to certain amino acids.

Amino acid	Codon	Anticodon
Alanine		CGC
Arginine	CGC	
Cysteine		ACA
Glutamic acid	GAA	
Glutamine		GUU
Glycine	GGC	
Isoleucine		UAU
Leucine	CUU	
Proline		GGC
Threonine	ACA	
Tyrosine		AUA
Valine	GUU	

Table 3.1

   a) Identify bases 1–9. (2)
   b) Name processes P and Q. (1)
   c) Copy and complete Table 3.1. (2)
   d) Give the triplet of bases that would be exposed on a molecule of tRNA to which valine would become attached. (1)
   e) Use your table to identify amino acids U, V, W, X, Y and Z. (2)
   f) i) Work out the mRNA code for part of a polypeptide chain with the amino acid sequence:
          threonine-leucine-alanine-glycine.
       ii) State the genetic code on the DNA strand from which this mRNA would be formed. (2)

3   Some amino acids can be synthesised by the body from simple compounds; others cannot be synthesised and must be supplied in the diet. The latter type are called the **essential amino acids**. The graph in Figure 3.3 shows the results of an experiment using rats where group 1 was fed zein (maize protein), group 2 was fed casein (milk protein) and group 3 was fed a diet that was changed at day 6.

   a) One of the proteins contains all of the essential amino acids, whereas the other lacks two of them.
       i) Identify each protein.
       ii) Explain how you arrived at your answer. (4)

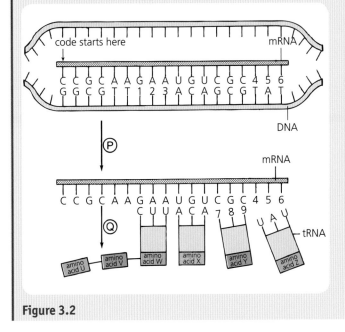

Figure 3.2

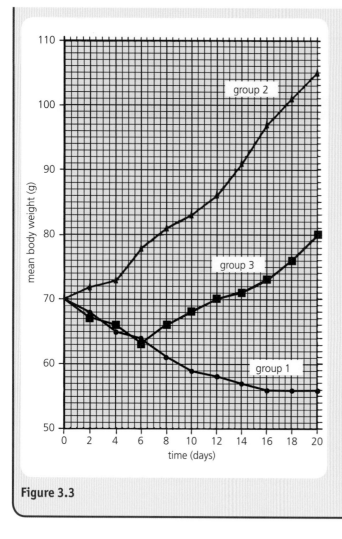

Figure 3.3

b) i) State which protein was given to the rats in group 3 during the first 6 days of the experiment.
   ii) Suggest TWO different ways in which their diet could have been altered from day 6 onwards to account for the results shown in the graph. (3)
c) By how many grams did the mean body weight of the rats in group 2 increase over the 20-day period? (1)
d) Calculate the percentage decrease in mean body weight shown by the rats in group 1 over the 20-day period. (1)

4 Give an account of translation of mRNA into a polypeptide. (9)

4 Genes and proteins in health and disease

1   A particular polypeptide chain was known to be 10
    amino acids in length. When enzymes were used to break
    down several molecules of it at three different places
    along its length, the fragments shown in Figure 4.1
    were obtained. (Note: AA = amino acid; N = one end of
    the polypeptide chain.) Draw a diagram of the complete
    polypeptide chain. (1)

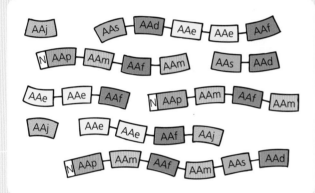

Figure 4.1

2   Human blood serum contains two major groups of
    protein: albumin and globulins. Some examples of
    these proteins are given in Table 4.1. Figure 4.2 shows a
    separation of serum proteins by electrophoresis and the
    results presented as a graph.

a) i)   Compared with the globulins as a group, do
        albumin proteins have a higher or a lower
        molecular weight?
   ii) Explain how you arrived at your answer. (2)
b) i)   Based only on the information given in Table 4.1,
        identify the specific group of blood proteins that
        could indicate liver disease if its concentration
        increased greatly.
   ii) From what condition might a person be suffering
        if the concentration of beta-globulins in her
        bloodstream increased to an abnormal level? (2)
c) i)   The graph in Figure 4.3 shows a patient's results
        from a serum protein electrophoresis test. From
        which of the following could this person be
        suffering? (Your answer should be based only on
        the information in Table 4.1.)
        A leakage of blood from vessels
        B cirrhosis of the liver
        C iron-deficiency anaemia
        D cancer of cells in bone marrow
   ii) Why is this diagnosis *not* conclusive? (2)

Blood protein group		Details
Albumin		It makes up more than half of the protein in blood serum and prevents blood from leaking out of vessels.
Globulins	Alpha-1-globulins (α1)	They include a high-density lipoprotein that contains 'good' cholesterol *not* taken into the artery wall.
	Alpha-2-globulins (α2)	They include a protein that binds with haemoglobin. Some of the proteins in this group are increased in concentration in conditions such as diabetes and cirrhosis of the liver.
	Beta-globulins (β)	They include a protein called transferrin that carries iron through the bloodstream and increases in concentration during iron-deficiency anaemia.
	Gamma-globulins (γ)	Many are antibodies whose numbers increase in response to viral invasion and some cancers such as myeloma (which affects bone marrow) and lymphatic leukaemia.

Table 4.1

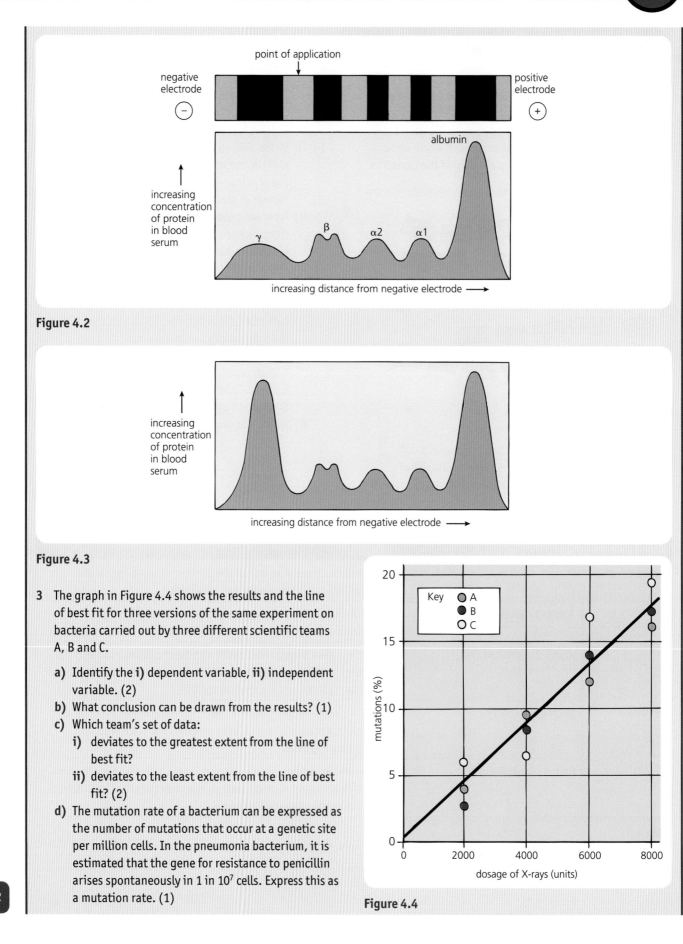

Figure 4.2

Figure 4.3

3 The graph in Figure 4.4 shows the results and the line of best fit for three versions of the same experiment on bacteria carried out by three different scientific teams A, B and C.

a) Identify the **i)** dependent variable, **ii)** independent variable. (2)

b) What conclusion can be drawn from the results? (1)

c) Which team's set of data:
   i) deviates to the greatest extent from the line of best fit?
   ii) deviates to the least extent from the line of best fit? (2)

d) The mutation rate of a bacterium can be expressed as the number of mutations that occur at a genetic site per million cells. In the pneumonia bacterium, it is estimated that the gene for resistance to penicillin arises spontaneously in 1 in 10^7 cells. Express this as a mutation rate. (1)

Figure 4.4

4 In the following three sentences, a small error alters the sense of the message. To which type of single-gene point mutation is each of these equivalent?

   a) Intended: She ordered boiled rice.
      Actual: She ordered boiled ice. (1)
   b) Intended: He walked to the pillar box.
      Actual: He talked to the pillar box. (1)
   c) Intended: He put a quid in his pocket.
      Actual: He put a squid in his pocket. (1)

5 Beta (β) thalassemia is caused by one of many different types of mutation that affect the HBB gene on chromosome 11. The HBB gene encodes beta-globin protein. Figure 4.5 shows the pattern of inheritance of one form of the genetic disorder where heterozygous carriers are mildly affected and individuals with a genotype homozygous for the mutant allele are severely affected.

Copy and complete the lower half of the diagram to show what would result, on average, in this cross. (4)

6 Figure 4.6 shows part of a metabolic pathway. Each stage is controlled by an enzyme. Some of the stages have been given a letter.

   a) Explain how a gene mutation can lead to a blockage in such a pathway. (2)
   b) Identify the letter that represents the point of blockage that leads to each of the following genetic disorders:
      i)   phenylketonuria
      ii) albinism (characterised by lack of brown melanin pigment in the skin)
      iii) alcaptonuria (characterised by an accumulation of homogentisic acid which is excreted in urine and turns black in light). (3)

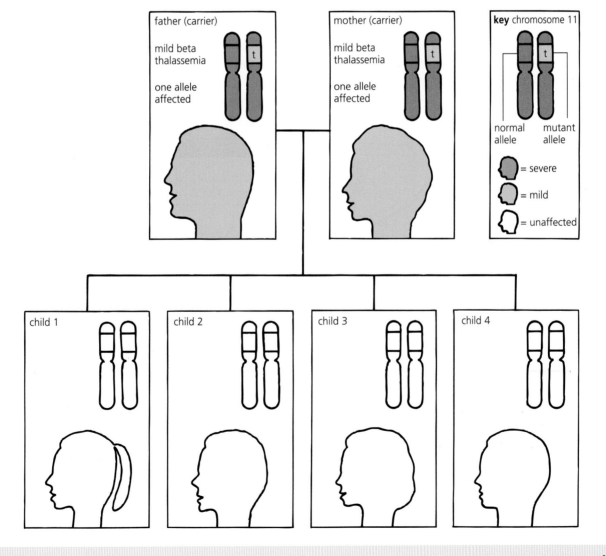

Figure 4.5

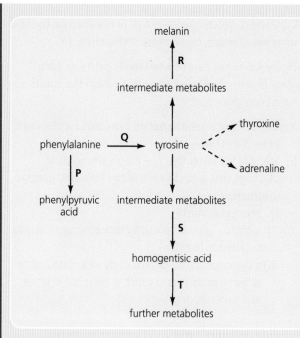

Figure 4.6

c) The graph in Figure 4.7 shows the effect of a phenylalanine meal on a normal person and on a sufferer of phenylketonuria (PKU).

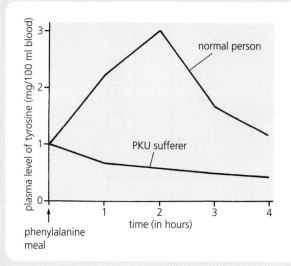

Figure 4.7

i) Explain the initial rise in level of tyrosine in the normal person.

ii) Why does the PKU sufferer not show a similar increase?

iii) Why does the level of tyrosine in the normal person fall after 2 hours? (3)

7 Read the passage and answer the questions that follow it.

Trinucleotide repeat expansion is caused by slippage during DNA replication which results in the formation of 'loop-out' structures. One group of genetic disorders is caused by an increased number of CAG codon repeats. These are translated into a tract of extra glutamines. In Huntington's disease (HD) the individual only becomes affected if the number of CAG repeats on chromosome 4 exceeds 35 copies. The greater the number of repeats present beyond this critical threshold, the more severe the disease and the earlier its onset. Individuals who have a history of HD in their family for many generations show an earlier age of onset and a faster progression of the condition in successive generations. This phenomenon is the result of further CAG codons being added and persisting at each generation.

Fragile X syndrome belongs to a different group of trinucleotide repeat disorders. It is caused by repeats of the CGG codon which affect a gene on the X chromosome. Table 4.2 shows the effect of increase in number of repeats of the codon.

Number of repeats of CGG codon present	State of individual with reference to fragile X syndrome
6–53	Unaffected
54–229	Normally unaffected
230–4000	Affected

Table 4.2

a) i) Identify the type of mutation that is the general theme of the passage.

   ii) Is this type of mutation a single-gene mutation or a chromosome structure mutation? (2)

b) Based only on information in the passage, construct a table to show THREE differences in genetic factors that exist between the two genetic disorders discussed. (3)

c) i) When a family has a long history of Huntington's disease, what TWO differences exist, on average, between sufferers of one generation and sufferers of the previous generation?

   ii) Explain why. (3)

8 During gamete formation, chromosomes normally form pairs that match one another, gene for gene, all along their length. The members of each pair of chromosomes shown in Figure 4.8 do not match properly because of a mutation.

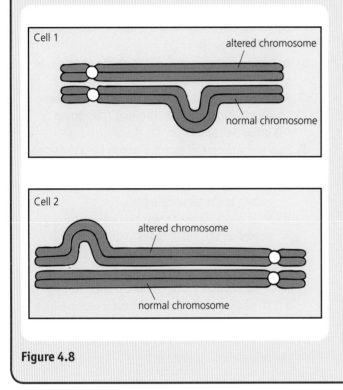

Figure 4.8

a) Which type of mutation has occurred in each case? (2)
b) i) Which of these would be more likely to prove lethal to the organism?
    ii) Explain your choice. (2)

9 Describe THREE types of single-gene point mutation and their effects on amino acid sequences. (9)

5 Human genomics

1 Figure 5.1 shows the DNA fragments that resulted from two copies of part of a genome, each cut by a different enzyme. The computer works out the sequence of the bases by looking for overlaps between the fragments. It found that the four larger fragments possessed overlaps. Draw a copy of these four larger fragments on squared paper, cut them out and use them to construct this part of the person's genome. (1)

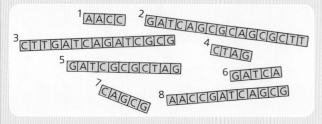

Figure 5.1

2 The genetic sequences for a protein-coding gene from the genomes of two people were compared. They were found to differ by three SNPs.
   a) Will the two people definitely differ in phenotype as a result of these differences? (1)
   b) Explain your answer. (1)

3 Genetic material from a sample of volunteers of differing ethnic origin was collected and analysed. Table 5.1 summarises the results and shows the SNPs (single nucleotide polymorphisms) that occur at six closely located sites on the genomes of these people. The results refer to a single strand of DNA.

   a) i) What is a single nucleotide polymorphism (SNP)?
      ii) Which site in the table appears to have been least affected by SNPs? (2)
   b) By how many bases at sites 1–6 do the genomes of groups 7 and 10 differ? (1)
   c) Which group(s) has the same set of bases at these six sites in its genome as: i) group 1; ii) group 2; iii) group 3? (3)
   d) How many people of ethnic origin W have the same genotype as people in group 9? (1)
   e) i) Which set of six bases occurs most frequently among the total sample group?
      ii) What percentage of the total sample group possesses this set of bases in its genome? (2)
   f) Which group has the least common set of bases in its genome? (1)
   g) If the set of bases in the genome possessed by group 6 is strongly associated with a fatal disease, which other groups are at equal risk? (1)
   h) What TWO things could be done to increase the reliability of the results? (2)

4 a) i) Figure 5.2 shows a tiny part of the human genome. Imagine that the 30 base pairs shown

Group	Ethnic origin	Number of individuals in group	Set of bases at six sites in the genome as a result of SNPs					
			Site 1	Site 2	Site 3	Site 4	Site 5	Site 6
1	W	1	C	C	T	A	T	G
2	W	17	T	C	C	A	C	A
3	W	63	T	T	C	A	C	A
4	W	21	C	T	T	A	T	G
5	X	44	T	C	C	A	C	A
6	X	36	C	T	T	A	T	G
7	X	1	C	C	T	A	T	G
8	X	1	T	T	C	A	C	A
9	Y	47	T	C	C	A	C	A
10	Y	1	T	C	C	G	C	A
11	Y	87	C	T	T	A	T	G
12	Y	1	C	C	T	A	T	G

Table 5.1

are printed on a strip of paper that is 100 mm in length. How many metres of paper strip would be required to print out the entire human genome if it is three billion base pairs in length?

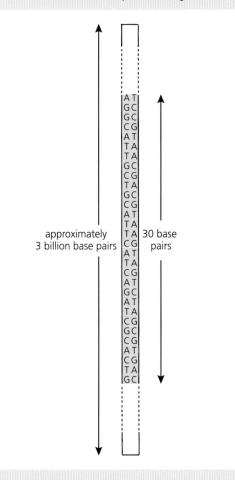

approximately 3 billion base pairs

30 base pairs

Figure 5.2

ii) Convert your answer to i) into kilometres and express it as words. (2)

b) i) Is the human genome that was completed in 2003 likely to be an exact match for any one individual?

ii) Explain your answer. (2)

5 Read the passage and answer the questions that follow it.

Debrisoquine hydroxylase is an enzyme made by cells in the liver. It is responsible for the breakdown of drugs used to treat a variety of disorders such as nausea, depression and heart disorders once the drugs have brought about their desired effect.

Several alleles of the gene that codes for this enzyme occur among the members of the human population.

These alleles code for different versions of the enzyme, which, in turn, vary in their ability to metabolise drugs. Depending on their particular genotype, a person may produce no functional enzyme and be a poor metaboliser because both of their alleles are null and void.

If the person has one null allele and one inferior allele that codes for a partly functional version of debrisoquine hydroxylase, they are said to be an intermediate metaboliser. An extensive metaboliser has one or two normal alleles that code for the fully functional form of the enzyme. Some people possess more than two copies of the normal allele and their metabolic profile is described as ultra-rapid.

a) Copy and complete Table 5.2 which summarises the passage. (4)

Alleles of gene present in genome	State of enzyme	Person's metabolic profile
	Non-functional	
One null allele and one inferior allele		
		Extensive
	Highly functional	

Table 5.2

b) What type of mutation could account for an ultra-rapid metaboliser having more than two copies of the allele of the gene that codes for debrisoquine hydroxylase? (1)

c) i) Which group of people are most likely to be at risk of harmful side effects if given a standard dose of a drug normally broken down by debrisoquine hydroxylase?

ii) Explain your answer. (2)

d) i) For which group of people would a standard dose of such a drug probably be ineffective?

ii) Explain your answer. (2)

e) In what way might personalised medicine (pharmacogenetics) solve the problems referred to in questions c) and d)? (2)

6 Figure 5.3 shows the DNA profiles (genetic fingerprints) of seven people.

  a) Identify the parents of person P. (1)
  b) Identify the monozygotic (identical) twins. (1)
  c) i) Could person P be the twins' brother?
    ii) Explain your answer. (2)
  d) i) Could the remaining two people in the diagram have the same parents as P?
    ii) Explain your answer. (2)

7 Give an account of personalised medicine under the headings:

  a) source of genomic information about a patient (4)
  b) possible benefits to the patient (3)
  c) possible disadvantages. (2)

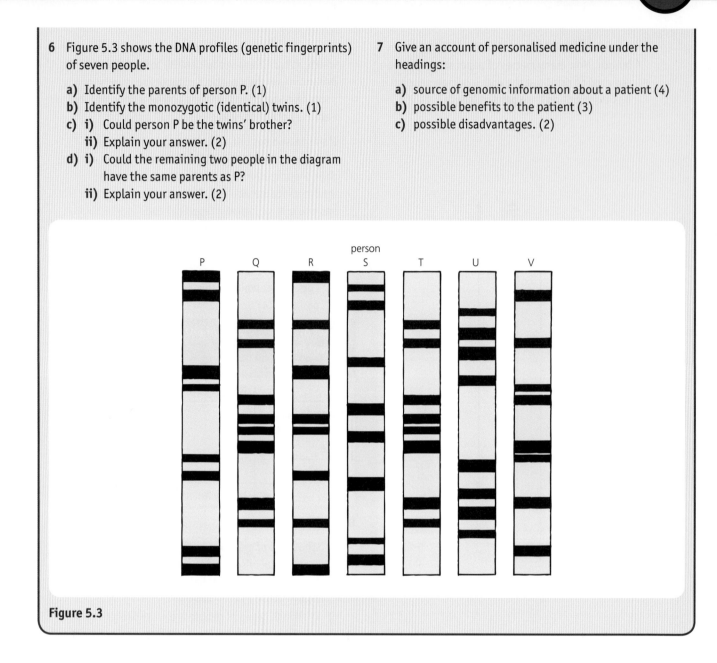

Figure 5.3

6 Metabolic pathways

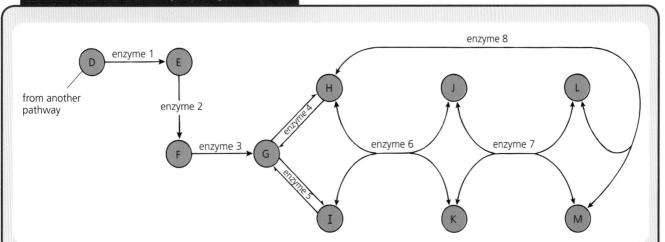

Figure 6.1

1 Figure 6.1 shows a metabolic pathway where each encircled letter represents a metabolite.
   a) How many of the reactions under enzyme control in this pathway are **i)** reversible, **ii)** irreversible? (2)
   b) Predict what would happen if metabolite I built up to a concentration far in excess of that of metabolite H. (2)
   c) **i)** By what alternative route could a supply of intermediates J and K be obtained if enzyme 6 becomes inactive?
      ii) By what alternative route could a supply of intermediates L and M be obtained if enzyme 8 becomes inactive?
      iii) By what alternative route could a supply of metabolite I be obtained if enzyme 5 becomes inactive? (3)
   d) Suggest a benefit to a living organism of its metabolic pathways possessing alternative routes. (1)

2 Figure 6.2 shows the stages that occur during an enzyme-controlled reaction.

   a) Which of these stages illustrate induced fit? (1)
   b) Using the letters given, indicate the correct sequence in which the four stages would occur if the enzyme were promoting:
      i) the build-up of a molecule from smaller components
      ii) the breakdown of a molecule into smaller constituents. (2)
   c) Which of the molecules shown in Figure 6.3 could act as a competitive inhibitor to this enzyme? (1)

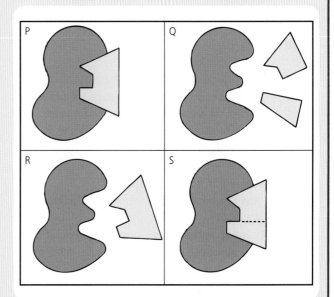

Figure 6.2

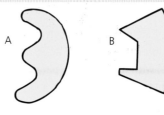

Figure 6.3

3 The graph shown in Figure 6.4 summarises the results from an experiment involving an enzyme-controlled reaction.

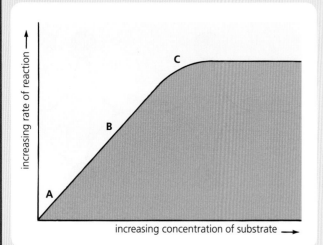

Figure 6.4

a) i) In this experiment, the enzyme concentration was kept constant. From the graph, identify the factor that was varied by the experimenter.
ii) Is this factor called the dependent or the independent variable?
iii) What effect did an increase in this factor have over region AB of the graph? (3)
b) Suggest which factor became limiting at point C on the graph. (1)
c) Which letter on the graph represents the situation where **i)** almost all of the active sites, **ii)** none of the active sites, **iii)** about half of the active sites on enzyme molecules are freely available for attachment to substrate molecules? (3)
d) Suggest what could be done to increase the rate of the reaction beyond the level it has reached at C. (1)

4 Tables 6.1 and 6.2 give the results from an experiment set up to compare the activity of an enzyme (alkaline phosphatase) with its substrate (para-nitrophenol phosphate) in the presence and absence of a competitive inhibitor.

Concentration of substrate (nmol/l)	Enzyme activity (units)
0	0.0
10	1.8
20	2.6
30	3.3
40	3.6
50	3.8
60	4.0
70	4.0

Table 6.1

Concentration of substrate (nmol/l) + inhibitor	Enzyme activity (units)
0	0.0
10	0.6
20	1.0
30	1.5
40	2.1
50	2.7
60	3.0
70	3.6

Table 6.2

a) i) Draw a curve of best fit for the results in Table 6.1.
ii) On the same graph, draw a line of best fit for the results in Table 6.2.
iii) Mark 'presence of inhibitor' and 'absence of inhibitor' on your graph to identify the lines. (4)
b) At which of the following ranges of substrate concentration (in nmol/l) did the enzyme activity increase at the fastest rate in the absence of inhibitor? (1)
  A 0–19 **B** 20–39 **C** 40–59
c) By how many times was enzyme activity at substrate concentration of 10 nmol/l greater when the inhibitor was absent? (1)

d) Calculate the percentage decrease in enzyme activity caused by the inhibitor at a substrate concentration of i) 20 nmol/l, ii) 70 nmol/l. (2)

e) Why would the two lines on the graph fail to meet even if higher concentrations of substrate were used? (1)

5 Figure 6.5 refers to changes in an allosteric enzyme that controls the rate of a reaction in a metabolic pathway.

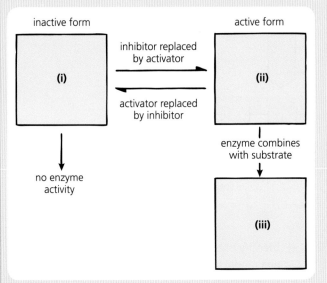

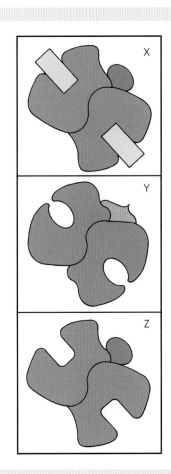

Figure 6.5

Figure 6.6

a) Match blank boxes i), ii) and iii) with diagrams X, Y and Z in Figure 6.6. (2)

b) Which of these lettered diagrams shows induced fit? (1)

c) Which of these lettered diagrams show an occupied allosteric site? (1)

d) Is the inhibitor that affects this enzyme *competitive* or *non-competitive*? (1)

c) In which tubes was the enzyme's activity inhibited? (1)

d) Which tubes made up the experiment and which tubes were the controls? (2)

e) i) Identify the inhibitor.
   ii) Did it act competitively or non-competitively?
   iii) Explain your choice of answer. (4)

6 The experiment shown in Figure 6.7 was set up to investigate the inhibitory effect of iodine solution on the action of β-galactosidase as the concentration of the substrate ONPG was increased.

a) In which tubes did the enzyme act on its substrate? (1)

b) Identify the independent variable in this experiment. (1)

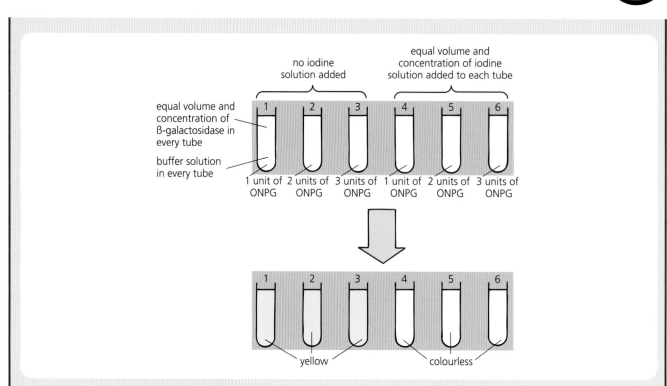

Figure 6.7

7   Figure 6.8 shows a metabolic pathway that occurs in cells of *E. coli*.

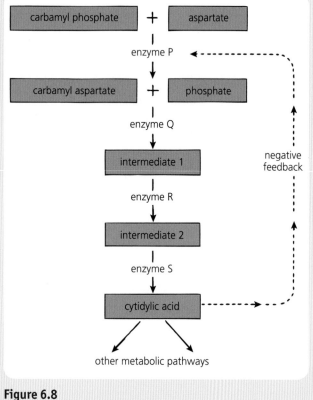

Figure 6.8

a) Identify enzyme P's i) substrates, ii) products, iii) end product inhibitor. (3)

b) i) If there is little or no demand for cytidylic acid for use in other metabolic pathways, what effect will this have on the concentration of carbamyl phosphate?

   ii) Explain your answer. (2)

c) i) If there is a high demand for cytidylic acid in other metabolic pathways, will the negative feedback process be increased or decreased?

   ii) Explain your answer. (2)

d) Which of the following statements is/are true? (1)

   A   The end product inhibits an early step in its own synthesis.

   B   The negative feedback mechanism regulates the rate of synthesis of metabolic intermediates.

   C   End product inhibition prevents the build-up of intermediates, which would be wasteful to the cell.

7 Cellular respiration

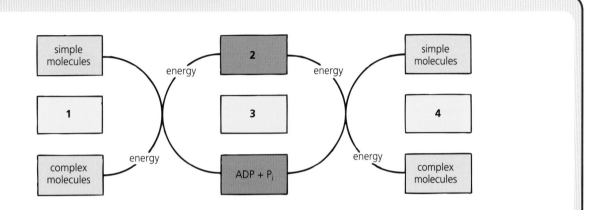

Figure 7.1

1   Metabolism falls into two parts:
    • **anabolism**, consisting of energy-requiring reactions that involve synthesis of complex molecules
    • **catabolism**, consisting of energy-yielding reactions in which complex molecules are broken down.

    Transfer of energy from catabolic reactions to anabolic reactions is brought about by **ATP**. Figure 7.1 is a summary of the above information.

    a) Copy the diagram and add four arrowheads to show the directions in which the two coupled reactions occur. (2)
    b) Complete boxes 1–4 using each of the terms given in bold print in the passage above. (2)
    c) State whether each of the following is an anabolic (A) or a catabolic (C) reaction:
       i)   destruction of a microbe by enzymes in lysosomes
       ii) formation of the hormone thyroxin in the thyroid gland
       iii) conversion of glycogen to glucose in muscle tissue
       iv) synthesis of nucleic acids. (4)

2   One mole of glucose releases 2880 kJ of energy. During aerobic respiration in living organisms, 44% of this is used to generate ATP. The rest is lost as heat.

    a) What percentage of the energy generated during aerobic respiration is lost as heat? (1)
    b) Out of a mole of glucose, how many kilojoules are used to generate ATP? (1)
    c) Name TWO forms of cellular work that the energy held by ATP could be used to carry out. (2)

3   Table 7.1 refers to the process of cellular respiration in the presence of oxygen.

    a) Copy the table and complete the blanks indicated by brackets. (5)
    b) Which stage consists of an energy investment phase followed by an energy payoff phase? (1)
    c) At which stage is *most* ATP produced per molecule of glucose? (1)
    d) At which TWO stages do the end products of fat digestion enter the pathway? (2)
    e) Which TWO stages would fail to occur in the absence of oxygen? (2)

Stage of respiratory pathway	Principal reaction or process that occurs	Products
Glycolysis	Splitting of glucose into [_____]	[_____], NADH and pyruvate
[_____] acid cycle	Removal of [_____] ions from molecules of respiratory [_____]	[_____], FADH$_2$, [_____] and ATP
[_____] transport chain	Release of [_____] to form ATP	ATP and [_____]

Table 7.1

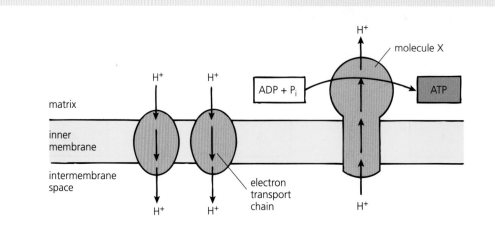

Figure 7.2

4 Figure 7.2 shows a small region of an inner mitochondrial membrane.

   a) i) Which side of the membrane has the higher concentration of H^+ ions?

     ii) Explain how this higher concentration of H^+ ions is maintained. (3)

   b) i) Name molecule X.

     ii) Briefly describe how it works. (3)

   c) Cyanide is a chemical that binds with the electron transport chains and brings the flow of high-energy electrons to a halt. Explain why cyanide is poisonous? (2)

5 Figure 7.3 shows, in a simple way, the molecular structure of three types of sugar. Table 7.2 shows the

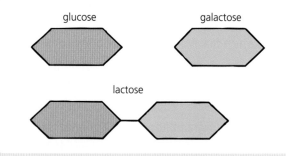

Figure 7.3

Time (min)	Total volume of carbon dioxide released (ml)		
	Glucose	Galactose	Lactose
0	0.0	0.0	0.0
10	0.0	0.0	0.0
20	0.5	0.0	0.0
30	3.0	0.5	0.5
40	6.0	1.0	0.5
50	11.0	1.5	1.5
60	16.0	1.5	1.5
70	18.0	2.0	2.0
80	32.5	2.0	2.5
90	39.5	2.0	3.0

Table 7.2

results of an investigation into the use by yeast of each of these sugars as its respiratory substrate.

a) Draw a line graph of the results on the same sheet of graph paper using three different colours. (4)

b) i) Identify the glucose result that was least reliable.
   ii) Justify your choice. (2)

c) What percentage increase in total volume of carbon dioxide released occurred for glucose between 20 minutes and 80 minutes? (1)

d) What conclusion can be drawn about yeast's ability to make use of each of the sugars as its respiratory substrate? (1)

e) i) What conclusion can be drawn about yeast's ability to break lactose down into its component sugars within the given time span?
   ii) Explain your answer. (2)

f) What could be done to improve the reliability of the results. (1)

g) Predict what the outcome would have been if the enzyme β-galactosidase had been added to each flask at the start of the experiment. (2)

6 Figure 7.4 shows a simplified version of several interconnecting metabolic pathways that occur in the human body. Questions a) and b) below both refer to the following four possible answers:

A B,E,M,P,U **B** G,I,K,M,N **C** A,E,N,R,Q **D** K,M,N,R,T

a) Which route would result in the synthesis of a complex molecule needed for tissue repair? (1)

b) Which route would lead on to the generation of much ATP by electron transport chains? (1)

c) i) Can a person build up and store fat if they consume excessive quantities of fat-free food over a long period?
   ii) Explain your answer with reference to Figure 7.4. (3)

d) How is it possible that a person can survive for many days without food? (2)

7 Give an account of the production of NADH and the role played by the electron transport chain during cellular respiration. (9)

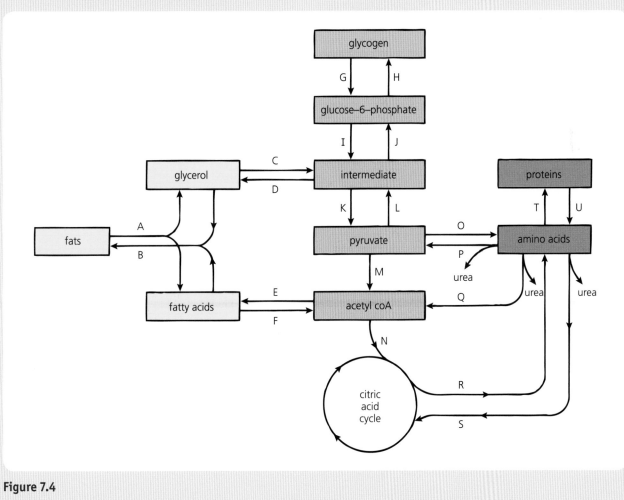

Figure 7.4

8 Energy systems in muscle cells

Event	Length of race (m)	Total energy expended (kJ)	Volume of oxygen taken in (dm³)	Energy from aerobic respiration (%)	Energy in anaerobic conditions (glycolysis) (%)
1	100	200	0	0	100
2	800	520	9	35	65
3	1 500	720	19	55	45
4	10 000	3 000	133	90	10
5	42 186	14 000	685	98	2

Table 8.1

1   The information in Table 8.1 is a set of mean values based on data obtained from many elite athletes.

   a) Present the data in the two columns referring to percentage of energy as a bar chart using two different colours. (3)

   b) Draw THREE conclusions from the data. (3)

   c) i)   Calculate the energy expended per metre by athletes performing in events 1 and 5.

      ii) By how many times is the energy expenditure greater in event 1 compared with event 5? (3)

2   The graph in Figure 8.1 shows the concentration of lactic acid in the blood of an athlete over a period of time.

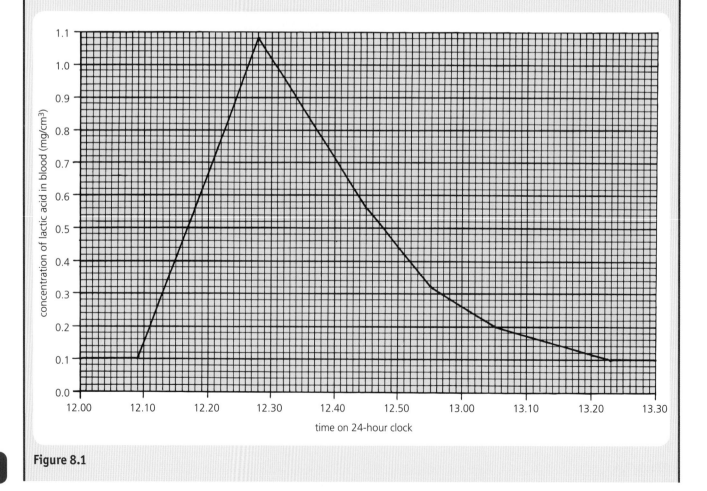

Figure 8.1

a) i) What was the concentration of lactic acid at 12.28?

ii) At which TWO times was the lactic acid concentration found to be 0.56 mg/cm³? (2)

b) i) Between which of the following four times did the athlete undergo 9 minutes of intensive exercise?

   A 12.00 and 12.10

   B 12.10 and 12.20

   C 12.20 and 12.30

   D 12.30 and 12.40

ii) Explain your choice of answer. (2)

c) i) By how many times was the concentration of lactic acid at 12.22 greater than that at 12.10?

ii) Between which of the following times did the lactic acid concentration decrease at the fastest rate?

   A 12.38 and 12.43

   B 12.48 and 12.53

   C 12.58 and 13.03

   D 13.08 and 13.13

iii) Calculate the percentage decrease in lactic acid concentration that occurred between 12.32 and 12.55. (Make your answer correct to two decimal places.) (3)

3 a) Describe the role played by the creative phosphate system during strenuous muscular activity. (3)

b) Give a comparison of slow twitch and fast twitch muscle fibres. (6)

Unit **2**

Physiology and
Health

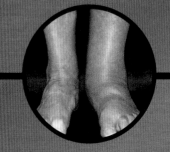

9 The structure and function of reproductive organs and gametes and their role in fertilisation and 10 Hormonal control of reproduction

1 Figure 9.1 shows a small part of an ovary and some of the stages that occur during maturation of a follicle.

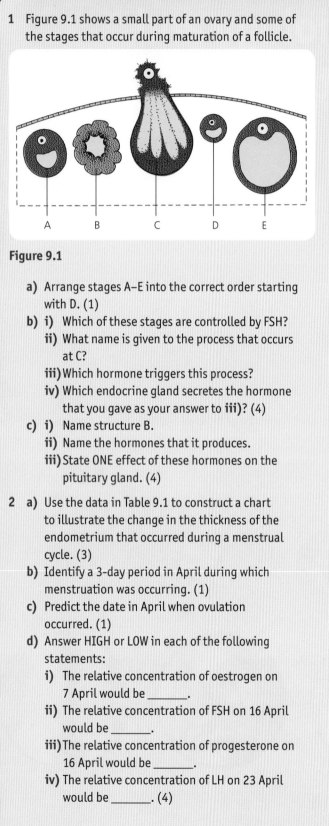

Figure 9.1

a) Arrange stages A–E into the correct order starting with D. (1)

b) i) Which of these stages are controlled by FSH?
ii) What name is given to the process that occurs at C?
iii) Which hormone triggers this process?
iv) Which endocrine gland secretes the hormone that you gave as your answer to **iii**)? (4)

c) i) Name structure B.
ii) Name the hormones that it produces.
iii) State ONE effect of these hormones on the pituitary gland. (4)

2 a) Use the data in Table 9.1 to construct a chart to illustrate the change in the thickness of the endometrium that occurred during a menstrual cycle. (3)

b) Identify a 3-day period in April during which menstruation was occurring. (1)

c) Predict the date in April when ovulation occurred. (1)

d) Answer HIGH or LOW in each of the following statements:
i) The relative concentration of oestrogen on 7 April would be _____.
ii) The relative concentration of FSH on 16 April would be _____.
iii) The relative concentration of progesterone on 16 April would be _____.
iv) The relative concentration of LH on 23 April would be _____. (4)

| Date | | Thickness of endometrium (mm) |
Month	Day	
March	26	4.2
	27	2.6
	28	1.8
	29	1.2
	30	1.6
	31	2.0
April	1	2.2
	2	2.4
	3	2.7
	4	3.0
	5	3.4
	6	3.7
	7	4.0
	8	4.4
	9	4.7
	10	5.0
	11	5.4
	12	5.7
	13	5.9
	14	6.0
	15	6.1
	16	6.2
	17	6.2
	18	6.2
	19	6.1
	20	6.0
	21	5.8
	22	5.4
	23	4.2
	24	2.6
	25	1.8

Table 9.1

3   A tiny part of the human testis is shown in microscopic
    detail in Figure 9.2.

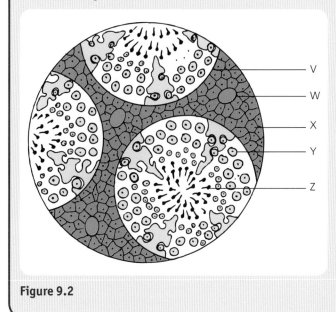

Figure 9.2

a) Name the parts labelled V, W, X, Y and Z. (5)
b) Which of these secretes testosterone? (1)
c) Which hormone from the pituitary stimulates these
    structures to produce testosterone? (1)
d) Briefly describe the means by which excessive
    production of testosterone is prevented? (3)

4   Give an account of the hormonal control of a menstrual
    cycle that does not involve fertilisation under the
    headings:

a) follicular phase (4)
b) luteal phase. (5)

11 Biology of controlling fertility

1 The data in Table 11.1 refer to four patients attending a fertility clinic.

	Patient			
	A	**B**	**C**	**D**
Total number of sperm (millions/cm³)	25	30	35	40
Number of active sperm (millions/cm³)	10	11	15	18
Number of normal sperm (millions/cm³)	15	16	22	24

Table 11.1

a) Present all of the data in Table 11.1 as a multicoloured bar chart. (3)

b) The clinic considers a man to be fertile if:
- over 20 million sperm are present in 1 cm³ of his semen
- at least 40% of his sperm are active
- at least 60% of his sperm are normal.

Which patient in the table fails to meet these criteria fully? (1)

2 Figure 11.1 shows a simplified version of the male reproductive system following a vasectomy.

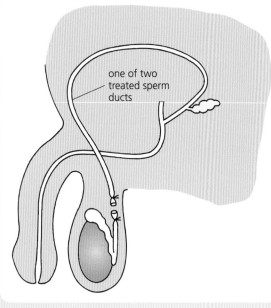

one of two treated sperm ducts

Figure 11.1

a) Explain how this works as a method of contraception. (1)

b) Suggest why vasectomy is more popular among middle-aged men than among men in their twenties. (1)

3 *In vitro* fertilisation often results in extra, unused fertilised eggs being kept in frozen storage. The very existence of these eggs raises many controversial issues. Briefly give your opinion of the following:

a) Should the extra eggs be destroyed after the mother has successfully given birth to a healthy baby?

b) Should the extra fertilised eggs be kept in storage in case the woman wishes to have more children?

c) i) Should the extra fertilised eggs be offered (with permission) to other women who are suffering fertility problems?

   ii) If so, who in your opinion are the legal parents of the children produced?

d) Should the extra fertilised eggs be made available to scientists to obtain stem cells for research?

4 Each pink arrow in Figure 11.2 indicates the point at which a certain method of contraception may act and prevent the sequence of events that leads to implantation from occurring. Match arrows 1–6 with the following methods of contraception. (5)

A condom

B contraceptive pill containing progesterone and oestrogen

C diaphragm

D intra-uterine device

E ligation of oviducts

F vasectomy

5 Give an account of the different ways in which infertility in humans may be treated. (9)

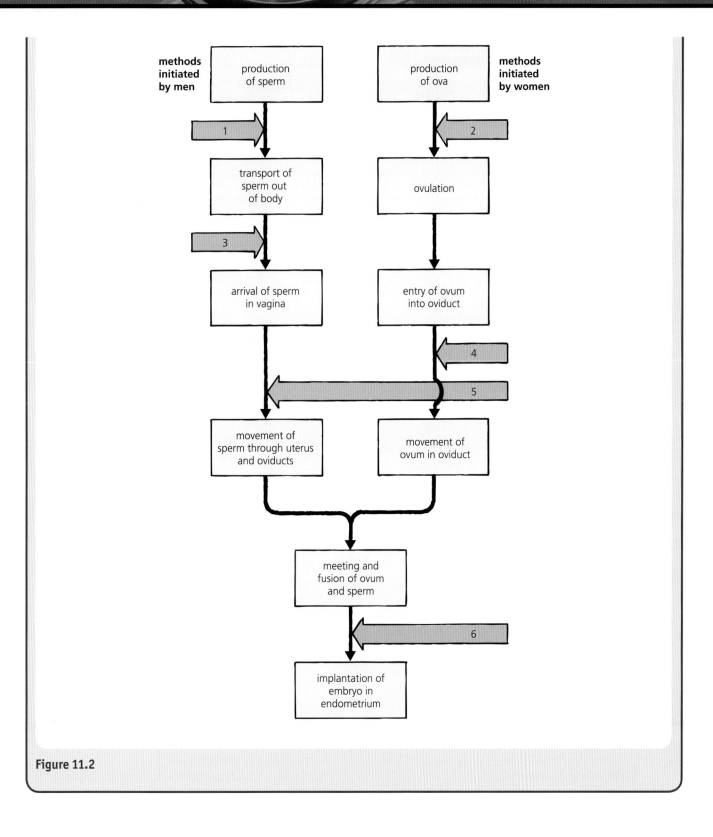

Figure 11.2

12 Ante- and postnatal screening

Chemical tested	Pregnancy trimester (3-month period)		
	First	Second	Third
Bilirubin	↓	↓	↓
AST (aspartate aminotransferase)	–	–	–
5′-nucleotidase	–	– or ↑	↑
ALT (alanine aminotransferase)	–	–	–
Albumin	↓	↓	↓
Alkaline phosphatase	–	– or ↑	↑
GGT (gamma-glutamyl transferase)	–	↓	↓
Serum bile acids (fasting state)	–	–	–

Table 12.1

Key: ↑ = increase, ↓ = decrease, – = no change (compared with non-pregnant women)

1 Table 12.1 indicates the effect of normal pregnancy on the concentration of several chemicals present in the woman's blood.

a) Which chemicals in the blood of women undergoing a normal pregnancy increase in concentration during the third trimester when compared with non-pregnant women? (1)

b) Which chemicals in the blood of women undergoing a normal pregnancy decrease in concentration during the third trimester when compared with non-pregnant women? (1)

c) Why is detection of elevation of aminotransferase levels regarded as a most useful indicator in the diagnosis of problems during pregnancy? (1)

d) Intrahepatic cholestasis of pregnancy (ICP) is a condition suffered by some pregnant women. It is characterised by intense itching and elevation of alkaline phosphatase and serum bile acid levels.

i) Which of these chemical changes can be used to test for the condition?

ii) Which of these chemical changes cannot be used to test for the condition?

iii) Explain your answer to ii). (3)

e) Suggest why a patient undergoes a period of fasting before a sample of her blood is taken to be tested for serum bile acids. (1)

2 Figure 12.1 shows a frequency distribution of human chorionic gonadotrophin (HCG) concentrations in pregnancies affected by Down's syndrome and unaffected pregnancies. (Note: the concentration of HCG is expressed as MoM. This means a multiple of the median for unaffected pregnancies at that gestational age.)

a) Which frequency distribution covers a greater range of HCG values? (1)

b) What percentage of i) unaffected pregnancies, ii) Down's syndrome pregnancies have an HCG value of 0.7? (2)

c) What percentage of i) unaffected pregnancies, ii) Down's syndrome pregnancies have an HCG value of 4? (2)

d) i) What is the most common HCG value for Down's syndrome pregnancies?

ii) What is the percentage frequency of affected pregnancies for this MoM value? (2)

e) i) Which HCG value occurs with the same frequency in both groups?

ii) State this frequency. (2)

f) i) Does an HCG level of 0.9 MoM exclude the risk of a Down's syndrome pregnancy?

ii) Explain your answer. (2)

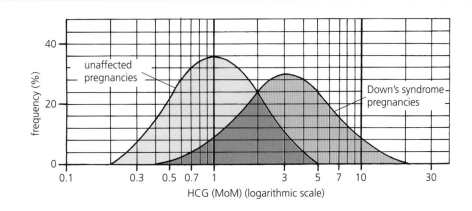

Figure 12.1

3   Following ultrasound scanning, the fetuses listed in Table 12.2 were all found to show a nuchal translucency (NT) of above normal thickness.

a) Some people are under the impression that women must be over the age of 35 to be carrying a fetus with Down's syndrome. What evidence from the table shows this impression to be wrong? (1)

b) Some people think that a thickened nuchal translucency indicates, for certain, that the fetus will suffer a chromosomal abnormality. How many fetuses in the table disprove this idea? (1)

c) The mother of which fetus went on to give birth to the live baby knowing that it would suffer Down's syndrome? (1)

d) Following the results of fetal karyotype analysis, what percentage of women, found to have a fetus with trisomy 21, chose to have the pregnancy terminated? (1)

Fetus number	Age of mother (years)	NT (mm)	Result of karyotype analysis	Outcome for fetus
1	22	5.4	Normal	Live birth
2	27	3.3	Trisomy 21	Termination of pregnancy at 16 weeks
3	28	3.7	Normal	Live birth
4	33	4.4	Normal	Live birth
5	35	7.4	Trisomy 21	Termination of pregnancy at 17 weeks
6	36	4.3	Trisomy 21	Termination of pregnancy at 16 weeks
7	36	3.9	Trisomy 21	Termination of pregnancy at 18 weeks
8	37	3.5	Normal	Live birth
9	38	8.1	Trisomy 21	Termination of pregnancy at 17 weeks
10	38	4.7	Trisomy 21	Live birth
11	40	5.6	Normal	Live birth
12	42	3.8	Trisomy 21	Termination of pregnancy at 16 weeks
13	43	3.4	Normal	Live birth
14	44	6.6	Trisomy 21	Dead at full term
15	45	5.9	Trisomy 21	Termination of pregnancy at 18 weeks

Table 12.2

4   Huntington's disease has a debilitating effect on the nervous system. It is caused by a dominant allele, which normally remains unexpressed until the person is over 30. Figure 12.2 shows two family trees involving this trait.

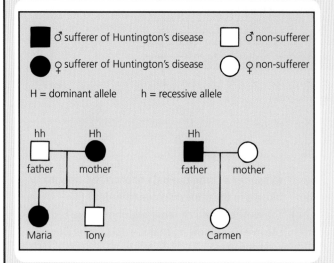

Figure 12.2

a) State the genotype of **i)** Maria, **ii)** Carmen's mother (who is aged 45). (2)

b) Carmen and Tony, both aged 21, intend to marry so they seek the advice of a genetic counsellor. He advises them that, depending on their genotypes, their children would be the result of one of the four situations shown in Table 12.3.

Possible situation	Carmen	Tony
A	Hh	Hh
B	Hh	hh
C	hh	Hh
D	hh	hh

Table 12.3

i) Why is the counsellor unable to state which of the four situations would arise?

ii) State the chance of a child from each of the four situations inheriting Huntington's disease. (5)

5   Figure 12.3 shows a pedigree chart for Duchenne muscular dystrophy.

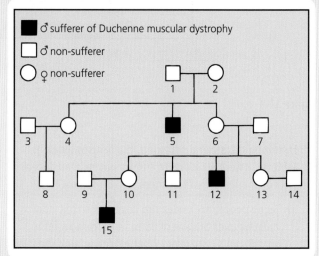

Figure 12.3

a) Which females are definitely carriers of the trait? (1)

b) What is the probability that person 13 is heterozygous for the trait? (1)

c) i) If couple 13 and 14 have a son, what is the chance, going on the information so far available, that he will suffer Duchenne muscular dystrophy?

ii) If couple 13 and 14 produce a son with Duchenne muscular dystrophy, what is the chance of their next son also being affected? (2)

6   Give an account of the uses of screening tests and diagnostic tests in antenatal care. (9)

13 The structure and function of arteries, capillaries and veins

1 By naming the heart chambers and the main blood vessels involved, describe the route taken by:
   a) an oxygen molecule absorbed into the blood at an alveolus in the lungs and transported to a kidney cell (5)
   b) a carbon dioxide molecule formed in a respiring brain cell and transported to an alveolus for removal. (5)

2 Figure 13.1 shows a transverse section of part of a vein and the outline for the equivalent part of an artery.

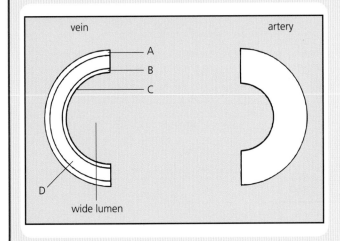

Figure 13.1

   a) Copy or trace the diagram and name parts A, B, C and D. (4)
   b) Complete the diagram to show the structure of an artery and label the parts. (4)
   c) i) State a further structural difference between the two types of vessel that is not shown in this diagram.
      ii) With the aid of simple diagrams, describe the role played by these structures. (4)

3 *Arteriole, artery, capillary, vein* and *venule* are five types of blood vessel. Using only these terms (but as often as you require), construct a flow chart to indicate the route taken by a red blood cell as it travels from a capillary bed in the body via the heart, lungs and heart again before returning to a capillary bed in the body. (4)

4 Table 13.1 shows the rate of blood flow in various parts of a person's body under differing conditions of exercise.
   a) What effect does increasingly strenuous exercise have on blood flow:
      i) in skeletal muscle?
      ii) to the gut?
      iii) Suggest the reason for the difference in each case. (4)
   b) Which other body part(s) shows the same trend in response to an increase in exercise as i) skeletal muscle, ii) gut? (2)
   c) i) Which body part's rate of blood flow remains unaffected by exercise?
      ii) Suggest why. (2)
   d) Briefly describe the mechanism by which blood vessels control distribution of blood to different parts of the body. (2)

5 The eight set-ups in Figure 13.2 show the apparatus used to investigate the elasticity of a ring of blood vessel.
   a) Which of the following pairs could be used to compare the effect of type of blood vessel on elasticity? (1)
      A 1 and 4   **B** 2 and 5   **C** 3 and 6   **D** 7 and 8
   b) Which of the following pairs should be compared to find out the effect of number of weights on the elasticity of a vein? (1)
      A 1 and 2   **B** 3 and 7   **C** 5 and 6   **D** 4 and 8

Part of body	Rate of blood flow (cm³/min)		
	At rest	Light exercise	Strenuous exercise
Skeletal muscle	1 200	4 500	12 500
Gut	1 400	1 100	600
Skin	500	1 500	1 900
Kidneys	1 100	900	600
Brain	750	750	750
Cardiac muscle	250	350	750

Table 13.1

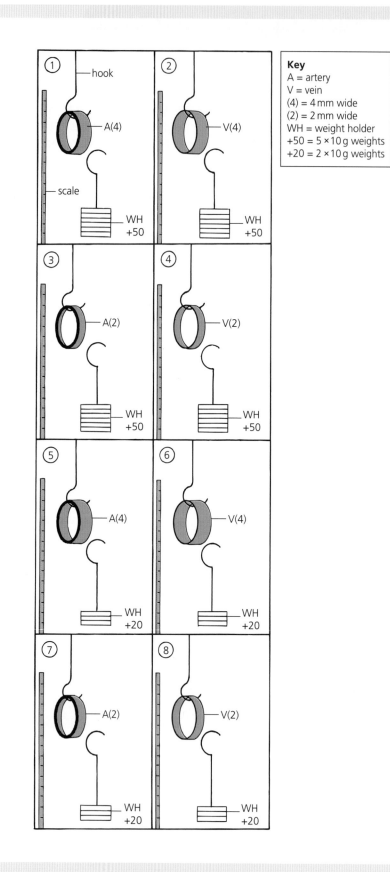

Figure 13.2

c) Which of the following pairs could be used to compare the effect of width of a ring on its elasticity? (1)

A 1 and 3 **B** 2 and 4 **C** 5 and 8 **D** 6 and 7

d) A comparison of 1 and 5 would indicate the effect of which of the following factors on elasticity of a vessel? (1)

A type of blood vessel
B width of ring of vein
C number of weights added
D thickness of vessel wall

6 Figure 13.3 shows part of the human circulatory system and the details of exchange of materials in a capillary bed.

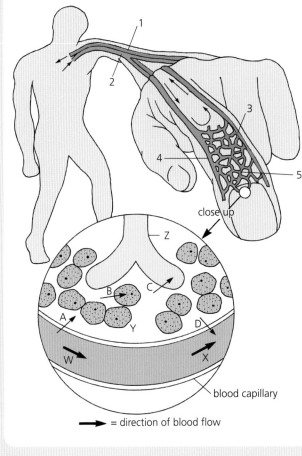

close up

blood capillary

→ = direction of blood flow

Figure 13.3

a) Name the different types of blood vessel numbered 1–5. (5)

b) In what way does blood pressure differ between points W and X in the diagram of the close-up? (1)

c) i) Name the liquid present in space Y.
ii) Describe how it is formed.
iii) Explain why the presence of this liquid is of importance to nearby cells.
iv) State ONE way in which the liquid differs from blood plasma. (4)

d) Identify structure Z and state its function. (2)

e) Which of arrows A–D represents the osmotic return of tissue fluid to the bloodstream? (1)

7 a) Show by means of an equation the relationship between heart rate (HR), cardiac output (CO) and stroke volume (SV). (1)

b) Calculate:
i) CO when HR = 72 beats/min and SV = 80 ml
ii) HR when SV = 85 ml and CO = 8.5 l/min
iii) SV when HR = 150 beats/min and CO = 15 l/min
iv) SV when HR = 125 beat/min and CO = 15 l/min. (4)

c) If situations **iii)** and **iv)** in **b)** refer to identical twins doing the same exercise, which one is fitter? Explain your answer. (2)

8 Give an account of the structure and function of the lymphatic system. (9)

14 Structure and function of the heart

1   The graphs in Figure 14.1 show the pressure changes that occur in the heart and associated blood vessels.
   a) i)   State the highest pressure exerted by each ventricle during the cycle.
      ii) With reference to the structure of the heart, explain the marked difference between these two pressures. (2)
   b) State the pressure at which the following valve movements occurred:
      i)   The right AV valve closed.
      ii) The SL valve opened.
      iii) The SL valve closed.
      iv) The left AV valve opened. (4)

   c) At what time in the cycle did ventricular systole begin? (1)
   d) Between which TWO times in the cycle did ventricular pressure exceed aortic pressure? (1)
   e) State the effect of diastole on the pressure of blood in the pulmonary artery. (1)

2   Read the passage and use the information that it contains to help you to match the answers that follow it with the blanks numbered 1–10 in Figure 14.2. (9)

Role of elastic walls

Although the ventricles do not contract during diastole, the blood pressure in the aorta does not drop to a low level. This maintenance of pressure is made

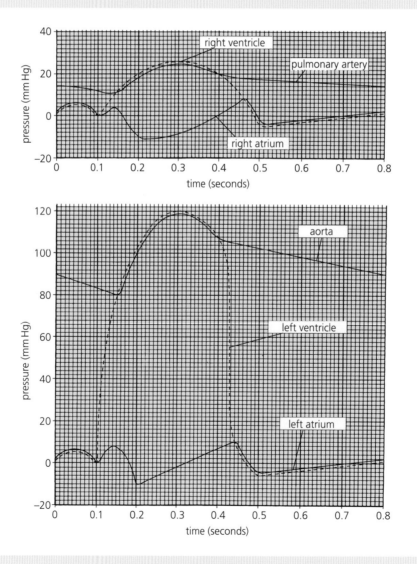

Figure 14.1

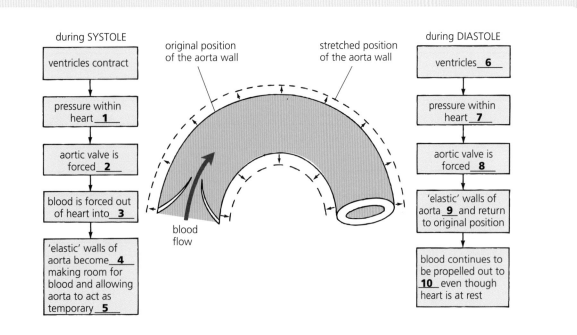

Figure 14.2

possible by the fact that the walls of the aorta (and large conducting arteries near the heart) are **elastic**, enabling them to stretch during ventricular systole. During ventricular diastole (with the SL valve closed), the elastic walls **recoil** and continue to propel blood through the vessels. A similar set of events occurs in the pulmonary artery.

aorta, body, decreases, increases, open, recoil, relax, reservoir, shut, stretched

3 a) Figure 14.3 shows a normal electrocardiogram containing waves X, Y and Z.

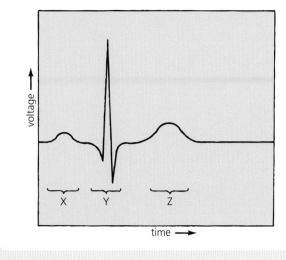

Figure 14.3

Which of these waves is produced during:
i)   electrical recovery of the ventricles?
ii) spread of electrical impulses across the atria?
iii) spread of electrical signals through the ventricles? (2)

b) Figure 14.4 shows two abnormal ECGs.

A

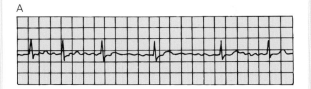

B

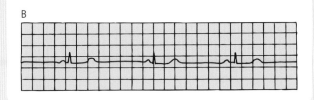

Figure 14.4

Which of these indicates:
i)   an abnormally slow heart rate?
ii) atrial fibrillation?
iii) Briefly explain your choice in each case. (4)

Part of circulatory system	Blood pressure (mm Hg)	Drop in pressure in this part of system (mm Hg)
	100	0
Aorta		
	95–100	
	85–95	
Arterioles		
	15–35	
	6–15	
Small veins		
Large veins	1–2	
	0–1	

Table 14.1

4 a) i) Copy Table 14.1 and complete the left column using the terms *capillaries, large arteries, left ventricle, small arteries, venae cavae* and *venules*.

   ii) Complete the other two columns. (6)

   b) i) In which TWO parts of the system do the greatest drops in pressure occur?

      ii) With reference to these parts only, state the total drop in pressure that occurs.

      iii) Account for this drop in pressure. (3)

5 Write notes on each of the following:

   a) the cardiac cycle (5)

   b) the conducting system of the heart. (4)

15 Pathology of cardiovascular disease

| Year | Deaths per 100 000 population from coronary heart disease | | | | | | | |
	Men aged 35–44	Women aged 35–44	Men aged 45–54	Women aged 45–54	Men aged 55–64	Women aged 55–64	Men aged 65–74	Women aged 65–74
1999	22	5	97	20	317	94	902	387
2000	19	5	92	20	291	84	823	347
2001	20	4	93	19	271	79	763	328
2002	21	4	89	19	250	72	707	304
2003	19	5	85	18	238	66	660	275
2004	19	4	81	16	219	57	599	250
2005	19	4	73	16	204	54	558	225
2006	18	4	72	15	194	52	500	207
2007	17	4	69	15	188	49	471	187
2008	17	4	67	14	175	47	443	179

Table 15.1

1 Table 15.1 shows death rates per 100 000 population from coronary heart disease in the UK. Draw THREE conclusions from the data. (3)

2 Table 15.2 shows part of a lipid profile table from the USA where cholesterol levels are measured in milligrams per decilitre (mg/dl). In the UK, cholesterol levels are measured in millimoles per litre (mmol/l). 1 mmol/l = 386.6 mg/l. 1 litre (l) = 10 decilitres (dl).

Convert the following values for Ian, a UK resident, and interpret his cholesterol levels. His HDL-cholesterol level is 1.56 mmol/l and his LDL-cholesterol level is 3.88 mmol/l. Show your working. (3)

3 The graph in Figure 15.1 shows the results of a survey on the effectiveness of four brands of statin (E, F, G and H) at bringing about a decrease in LDL-cholesterol in the bloodstream.

a) What daily dose of E brings about a decrease in LDL-cholesterol of 2.2 mmol/l? (1)

b) What decrease in LDL-cholesterol is brought about by a dose of 10 mg of H? (1)

c) What daily dose of i) F, ii) H would have the same effect as 40 mg of G? (2)

d) Which brand of statin produces the least overall decrease in LDL-cholesterol compared with the others? (1)

e) Which TWO brands of statin show no overlap in range of values of LDL-cholesterol decrease regardless of daily dose? (1)

f) i) Assuming that all four brands are equally priced and equally safe to use, which one is the best value for money?

ii) Explain your answer. (2)

HDL-cholesterol level (mg/dl)	LDL-cholesterol level (mg/dl)	Interpretation by experts
60 or more	60–129	Desirable
40–59	130–159	Borderline
39 or less	160–199	Heightened risk

Table 15.2

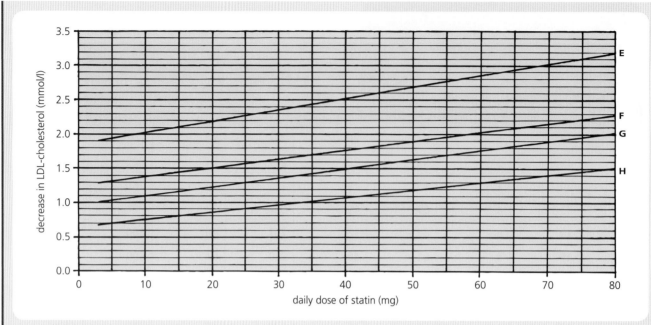

Figure 15.1

Age (years)	Expected percentage decrease in incidence of CVD						
	Projected decrease in LDL-cholesterol (mmol/l) brought about by statins						
	0.6	1.0	1.4	1.8	2.2	2.6	3.0
50	39%	56%	68%	77%	84%	88%	91%
60	27%	41%	52%	61%	68%	74%	79%
70	20%	31%	41%	49%	56%	62%	67%

Table 15.3

4 Table 15.3 shows the varying values of percentage decrease in incidence of CVD (cardiovascular disease) that some medical experts predict will result from decreases in level of LDL-cholesterol brought about by statin treatment. What TWO trends do the data forecast? (2)

5 Figure 15.2 shows a family tree (pedigree) for familial hypercholesterolaemia (FH) where H (the mutant allele for this inherited condition) is dominant to h (the allele for the unaffected state).

a) Identify **i)** a man who is unaffected by FH, **ii)** a woman who is a sufferer of FH. (2)
b) Give the genotype and phenotype of **i)** person M, **ii)** person X. (2)
c) **i)** Identify the person whose genotype cannot be worked out from the information given.
   ii) Explain your answer. (2)

d) If person Y marries a man with the same genotype as her father, what is the chance that each of their children will be **i)** a sufferer of FH, **ii)** unaffected by FH? (2)
e) Identify one piece of evidence from the pedigree that shows that FH is *not* a sex-linked trait. (1)

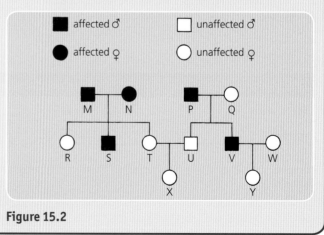

Figure 15.2

16 Blood glucose levels and obesity

1 An alternative method of illustrating the regulation of blood glucose level is shown in Figure 16.1.

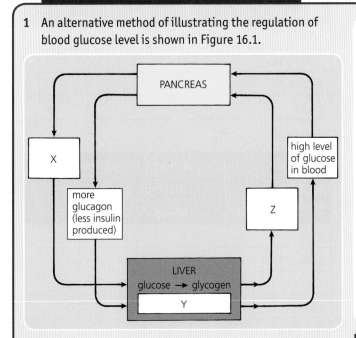

Figure 16.1

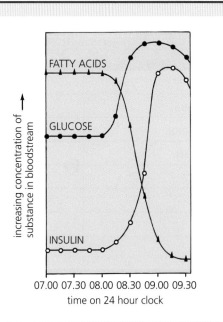

Figure 16.2

a) Redraw the diagram and complete blank boxes X, Y and Z. (3)

b) Copy and complete the following paragraph using the answers that follow it.
   The diagram has been drawn as two interrelated circuits to show that a _____ factor under _____ control is constantly wavering on either side of its _____ value. When it _____ from the norm, it is returned to this value by negative _____ control. If it overshoots the mark, a _____ set of mechanisms is triggered that returns the factor to its norm. If it now overshoots the mark in the opposite direction, the opposite set of _____ is made and so on.
   deviates, feedback, homeostatic, normal, physiological, responses, reverse (6)

2 Figure 16.2 shows the effect of consuming 50 g of glucose (after a period of fasting) on the concentrations of fatty acids, glucose and insulin in the bloodstream of a person who is not a diabetic.

a) i) During which period of time was the person's blood glucose concentration at a steady level?
   ii) By what means is this steady level maintained? (2)

b) i) At what time was the glucose consumed?
   ii) What initial effect did this intake have on blood glucose level and concentration of insulin in the blood?

iii) Why was there a short time lag between these two effects? (4)

c) Fatty acids are the breakdown products of fats.
   i) Does the information in the graph suggest that insulin promotes or suppresses the breakdown of stored fat?
   ii) Explain your answer to i). (2)

d) i) Redraw the axes and extend the time scale to 11.00 hours. Draw the glucose curve to show the concentration from 07.00 to 11.00 hours.
   ii) State TWO ways in which the glucose tolerance curve for a sufferer of uncontrolled diabetes would differ from the one that you have drawn. (4)

e) Suggest why the average birth weight of babies born to diabetic mothers is significantly higher than that of non-diabetic mothers. (Do not attempt to give a genetic explanation in your answer.) (1)

3 How many weeks would it take a person to lose 5 kg of body fat if their total energy output exceeded their total energy input by i) 840 kJ/day, ii) 2100 kJ/day? (Note: 1 kg of body fat contains 29.4 MJ of energy.) (2)

4 Tables 16.1–16.9 comprise a 10-year risk calculator for coronary heart disease (CHD).

SCORE CARD	
Feature	**Risk points**
Age	
LDL-cholesterol	
HDL-cholesterol	
Blood pressure	
Diabetes	
Smoker	
Total	

Table 16.1

Age (years)	Risk points
30–34	−1
35–39	0
40–44	1
45–49	2
50–54	3
55–59	4
60–64	5
65–69	6
70–74	7

Table 16.2

Concentration of LDL-cholesterol (mmol/l)	Risk points
<2.60	−3
2.60–4.14	0
4.15–4.92	1
>4.92	2

Table 16.3

Concentration of HDL-cholesterol (mmol/l)	Risk points
<0.91	2
0.91–1.16	1
1.17–1.55	0
>1.55	−1

Table 16.4

Risk points associated with blood pressure				
Systolic (mm Hg)	Diastolic (mm Hg)			
	<85	85–89	90–99	>99
<130	0	1	2	3
130–139	1	1	2	3
140–159	2	2	2	3
>159	3	3	3	3

Table 16.5

Diabetes	Risk points
Present	2
Absent	0

Table 16.6

Smoker?	Risk points
Yes	2
No	0

Table 16.7

Total number of risk points	10-year CHD risk (%)
≤−3	1
−2	2
−1	2
0	3
1	4
2	4
3	6
4	7
5	9
6	11
7	14
8	18
9	22
10	27
11	33
12	40
13	47
≥14	≥56

Table 16.8

Age (years)	Average 10-year CHD risk (%)
30–34	3
35–39	5
40–44	7
45–49	11
50–54	14
55–59	16
60–64	21
65–69	25
70–74	30

Table 16.9

Joe is a 49-year-old diabetic whose blood pressure is 129/84. He smokes 20 cigarettes daily and is slightly overweight but takes regular exercise. The last time his cholesterol levels were checked, his LDL-cholesterol was 4.58 mmol/l and his HDL-cholesterol was 1.05 mmol/l.

a) Calculate Joe's 10-year CHD risk using the risk calculator. (1)
b) Compare Joe's 10-year CHD risk with the average value. (1)
c) What advice would you give Joe in the light of these findings? (1)

Unit 3

Neurobiology and Communication

17 Divisions of the nervous system and parts of the brain

1 Copy and complete Figure 17.1, which shows two ways of classifying the parts of the human nervous system. (5)

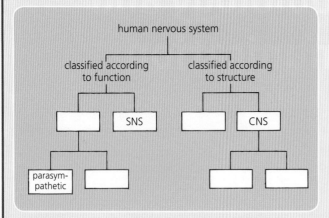

Figure 17.1

2 Imagine a person taking a carefree stroll through a field on a summer's day. Suddenly a bull appears from behind a hedge and charges towards the person. She runs for her life and just manages to escape in time.
 a) With reference to BOTH parts of the autonomic nervous system, briefly describe the events occurring in the person's body during and immediately after this crisis. (4)
 b) Predict the possible outcome to a person if the parasympathetic system took control of the body on a permanent basis. (1)

3 Figure 17.2 shows a simplified version of the sympathetic nerve supply to two parts of the body containing smooth involuntary muscle.

 a) i) Predict the effect of nerve impulses on the smooth muscle of the arteriole supplying blood to the gut.
  ii) What effect will this have on the bore of the tube?
  iii) Why is this response of survival value to the body during a crisis? (3)
 b) i) Predict the effect of sympathetic nerve impulses on the muscle making up the stomach's sphincter valves.
  ii) By what means could the reverse effect be brought about?
  iii) Under what circumstances would this reverse effect be of advantage to the body? Explain why. (4)

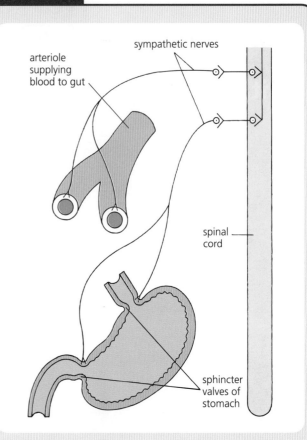

Figure 17.2

4 a) i) Copy and complete Figure 17.3, which represents part of the system by which breathing is controlled in the human body.
  ii) Why is such control of benefit to a human being. (8)
 b) The data in Table 17.1 refer to the results from an investigation into breathing.

Carbon dioxide in inspired air (%)	Average depth of breathing (cm³)	Average number of breaths per minute
0.04	673	14
0.79	739	14
1.52	794	15
2.28	911	15
3.11	1 232	15
5.48	1 848	16
6.02	2 104	27

Table 17.1

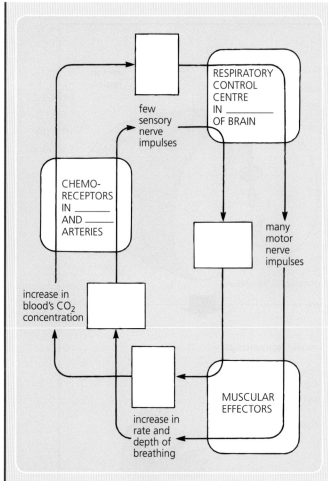

Figure 17.3

i) Plot the data to give two line graphs on the same sheet of graph paper.

ii) What variable factor was studied in this investigation?

iii) Make a generalisation about the effect of the variable factor on breathing.

iv) Which was affected first, rate or depth of breathing? (7)

5 Each part of the body capable of sending sensory impulses to the brain is represented by an area on the somatosensory region of each cerebral hemisphere. However, the area of the brain devoted to each body part is found to be in proportion not to the actual size of the body part but to the relative number of sensory receptors present in that body part (see Figure 17.4). Each cerebral hemisphere also possesses a motor region that controls body movements. Here the area of the brain allocated to each body part is related not to the body part's size but to its degree of mobility.

a) Name TWO types of sensation perceived by the sensory area of the cerebrum. (2)

b) Account for the fact that a leg is a big part of a normal human body, yet it is represented by a fairly small area on the cerebrum's sensory region. (1)

c) Which body part contains most sensory receptors relative to its actual size? (1)
   A trunk   B shoulder   C hip   D tongue

d) Which of the following structures has fewest nerve endings in relation to its actual size? (1)
   A arm   B face   C fingers   D lips

e) Match the areas marked X, Y and Z in Figure 14.4 with: brow, lips and foot. (2)

f) With reference only to the pinna (ear flap), predict how 'motor homunculus' would differ if a cat had been drawn. Explain your answer. (2)

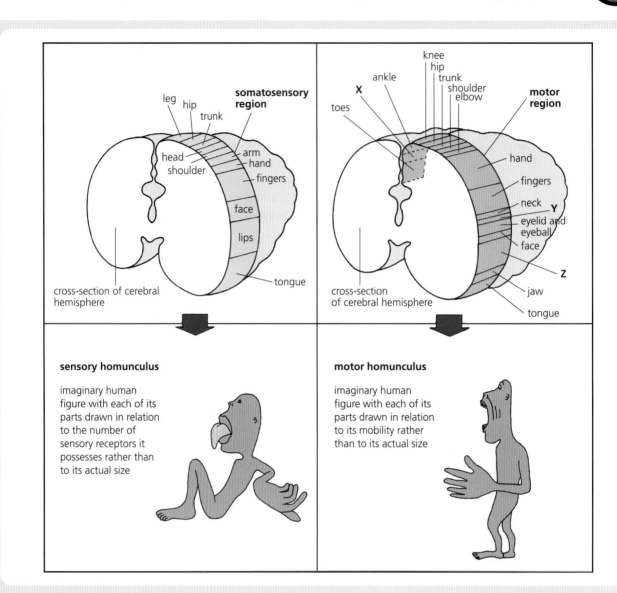

Figure 17.4

6 Figure 17.5 is a composite picture that was shown to several split-brain patients. A little later the patients were asked to study the four pictures shown in Figure 17.6.

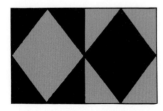

Figure 17.5

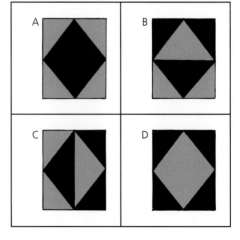

Figure 17.6

State, with reasons, which picture all of the patients chose when asked to:
a) say what they had seen (2)
b) point with their left hand to what they had seen. (2)

7 Figure 17.7 shows a map of the brain's language areas in the left cerebral hemisphere.

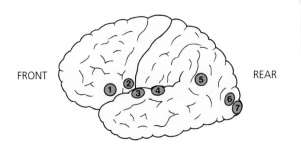

FRONT   REAR

Figure 17.7

a) Which TWO areas would show highest activity while the person was listening to and understanding a conversation on a mobile phone? (2)
b) Suggest what the person is doing when a high level of activity is registered in the following language areas in the order shown:
   i) 7, 6, 5, 4
   ii) 7, 6, 5, 4, 1, 2. (2)
c) Identify the areas involved and state their correct sequence of involvement when a spoken message is heard and then repeated out loud. (1)
d) Suggest what effect severe damage to region 1 in Figure 17.7 would have on the ability to
   i) understand language, ii) speak language. (2)

8 Read the passage and answer the questions that follow it.

Neurons in the brain show a high rate of metabolic activity and depend on the bloodstream for the delivery of a constant supply of oxygen. A **stroke** involves the blockage and/or rupture of a blood vessel that previously supplied a region of the brain with blood. This leads to the death of some brain cells and the loss (temporary or permanent) of some faculty. 80–90% of survivors, for example, are left with serious motor weakness of some part of the body.

An investigation was carried out to explore the effect of rehabilitative exercise on the ability of the brain to regain a function. Five right-handed men, who had suffered a stroke at least 6 months before the trial,

were chosen. Each had been left after the stroke with limited use of his right hand. During the investigation, each patient used his right hand to squeeze a specially designed device for an hour a day, 3 days a week for 4 weeks.

Functional magnetic resonance imaging (fMRI) measures tiny changes in oxygen concentration of blood in a region of the brain that is active. Figure 17.8 shows diagrams of a typical set of fMRI scans while the person was performing the task. The fMRI scans were carried out before and upon completion of the period of training and one month after training was complete.

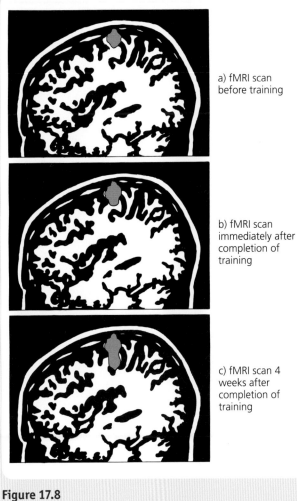

a) fMRI scan before training

b) fMRI scan immediately after completion of training

c) fMRI scan 4 weeks after completion of training

Figure 17.8

a) Why does a stroke cause damage to a part of the brain? (1)
b) i) Which side of the brain had been affected by the stroke suffered by each of the patients chosen for the investigation?
   ii) Explain your answer. (2)

→

c) Why was an fMRI scan carried out *before* the training period? (1)

d) Relate the orange areas in Figure 17.8 with the motor region in Figure 17.4 and explain why the orange areas are the ones picked up during the fMRI scans. (2)

e) What tentative conclusion can be drawn from Figure 17.8 about the effect of exercise on the ability of the brain to regain a function? (1)

f) i) What tentative conclusion can be drawn from Figure 17.8 about the ability of the brain to retain a function that it has regained?

   ii) Explain your answer. (2)

g) i) Give THREE examples of factors that limit this investigation and prevent scientists from drawing a general conclusion about the effect of rehabilitative exercise on the ability of the brain of stroke sufferers to regain the function of control of hand movement.

   ii) Suggest THREE ways of broadening the investigation to overcome these limitations. (6)

18 Perception and memory

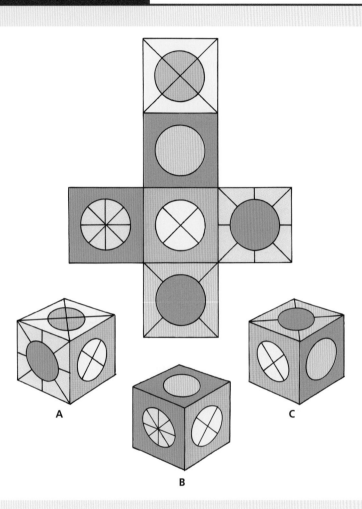

Figure 18.1

1 'Perception allows us to segregate objects from one another and recognise them.' Use your powers of perception (and any other skills that you possess) to decide which of the three boxes in Figure 18.1 has been opened up. (1)

2 Read the passage and answer the questions that follow it.

Babies learn to crawl at about the age of 6 months. Figure 18.2 shows the **visual cliff experiment**, which was set up to investigate if babies that are able to crawl can perceive depth. The special table used was composed of two chequerboard-patterned halves under a sheet of strong glass: one directly beneath the glass, the other a metre below it.

The latter gave the impression of a deep drop, although the glass top really provided a solid, safe surface. Thirty-six babies varying in age from 6 to 14 months

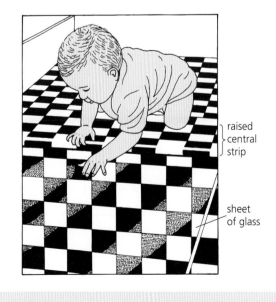

Figure 18.2

were individually placed on the raised central strip and encouraged to crawl over the 'cliff' to the 'deep' side by calls from their mother. The babies peered through the glass and some patted it with their hands but the vast majority refused to crawl onto the 'deep' side and moved back to the 'shallow' side.

a) Why were as many as 36 babies used? (1)
b) Why were an equal number of male and female babies used? (1)
c) Why was each baby placed on the visual cliff on their own? (1)
d) Identify THREE conditions that should be kept constant in this type of investigation. (3)
e) Why were the scientists unable to use babies under the age of 6 months? (1)
f) The scientists concluded that depth perception is an innate (inborn) ability.
   i) Were they justified in drawing this conclusion?
   ii) Explain your answer. (2)

3 In an investigation, volunteers were divided into two groups, X and Y. They were each given prior treatment, in turn, as indicated in the table in Figure 18.3 and then shown the appropriate ambiguous image for 30 seconds. Each person was next asked to draw their perception of the image and identify it.

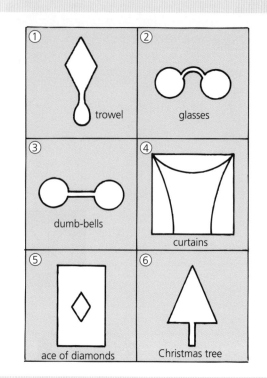

Figure 18.4

a) Figure 18.4 shows typical results from this investigation and these are considered to be the result of perceptual set. Match treatments A–F with results 1–6. (5)

Prior treatment		Ambiguous image
Group X	Group Y	
(A) Viewing of pictures featuring houses with many windows and doors	(B) Viewing of pictures of people playing cards at blackjack tables in casinos	
(C) Viewing of pictures featuring opticians' shops and advertisements for spectacles	(D) Viewing of pictures of weightlifters in action in gymnasia	
(E) Viewing of pictures of plantations of forests of coniferous trees	(F) Viewing of pictures of plasterers at work on walls and ceilings	

Figure 18.3

b) Figure 18.5 shows an ambiguous picture relating to a face and a fried breakfast. Briefly describe how this could be used to investigate if hunger affects perceptual set. (3)

Figure 18.5

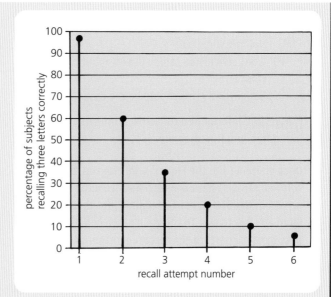

Figure 18.1

4 The plastic card used to release money from a bank's cash dispensing machine has a PIN (personal identification number) known only to the owner. Suggest why banks decided to give each PIN **four** digits. (2)

5 00349544423317 is the phone number of a hotel in the centre of Seville, Spain, when phoned from Britain. Analysis of this series of numbers shows it to be made up of the parts shown in Table 18.1.

International code	Code for Spain	Code for Seville	District of city	Hotel number
00	34	954	442	3317

Table 18.1

Imagine that this hotel is about to be telephoned from Britain by:

a) a person who has never phoned Spain before
b) a travel agent who regularly phones Seville's city centre hotels.
   Predict which person will be faster at placing the call and explain your answer. (2)

6 In an experiment to investigate the effect of lack of rehearsal on memory, some students listened to a group of three unrelated letters being read out. They were asked to try to recall the letters at 3-second intervals but were asked to count backwards in threes from 99 (99, 96, 93, etc.) during each of the intervals between recall attempts. Figure 18.1 shows the results.

a) What was the purpose of asking students to count backwards in threes from 99 between recall attempts? (1)
b) i) What percentage of students were able to correctly recall the three letters 6 seconds after attempt number 1?
ii) At which recall attempt did 80% of the students fail to recall the correct answer? (2)
c) Figure 18.2 shows a graph of the results from the control experiment. In what way would the instructions given to the control subjects differ from those given to the subjects involved in the original experiment? (1)

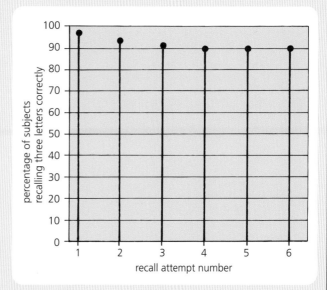

Figure 18.2

d) i) State the factor under investigation in the original investigation.

ii) What conclusion can be drawn about the effect of this factor?

iii) Suggest why this should be the case. (3)

7 Present the information contained in the following paragraph as a flow diagram. (3)

Once an item (e.g. the French words for the request 'Two coffees, please') has been retrieved from the LTM and is back in the STM, it can be recalled into the conscious mind and put to use. In this case nerve impulses would pass to those parts of the cerebrum responsible for language. Once certain mental and motor operations had occurred, the words would be spoken to the French waiter patiently awaiting the person's order.

8 The accompanying list **a)–h)** gives eight instructions that, according to experts, aid the processes of memory and learning if put into practice. Rewrite them and complete the blanks using the following words:

attention, groups, long, meaning, overlearn, recreation, repeating, rest, short, unusual, visual. (10)

a) Pay close _____ to the information to be memorised.

b) Organise items to be learned into _____.

c) Rehearse items by _____ them over and over to yourself.

d) Elaborate the _____ of a difficult item.

e) Create a _____ image of a group of unrelated items (the more _____ the image, the better).

f) _____ the information well beyond the point of bare recall rather than risk underlearning it.

g) Spread the learning process over several _____ sessions rather than one _____ one.

h) Use breaks from study for _____ and _____.

9 Give an account of the factors that promote:

a) the transfer of information from the STM to the LTM (6)

b) the retrieval of stored information from the LTM. (3)

19 The cells of the nervous system and neurotransmitters at synapses

1 Figure 19.1 shows the reflex arc involved in the withdrawal of the arm when the hand touches a naked flame.

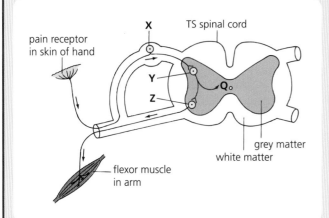

Figure 19.1

a) Identify neuron types X, Y and Z. (3)

b) Rewrite the following sentence to include only the correct word from each underlined choice.
When the reflex action of limb withdrawal occurs, this involves the <u>somatic/autonomic</u> nervous system and the type of response is described as <u>voluntary/involuntary</u>. (2)

c) Suggest where the impulse passing along route Q could be going to. (1)

2 Copy and complete Figure 19.2, which shows a simplified version of a reflex arc involving three neurons. (5)

3 Figure 19.3 shows the events involving a neurotransmitter that occur at a synapse during the transmission of a nerve impulse. Arrange them into the correct order, starting with stage E. (1)

4 The graphs in Figure 19.4 represent four types of multiple sclerosis (MS). Match them with the following descriptions. (3)
a) A primary, progressive form of MS involving steady increase in disability without attacks.
b) A 'benign' form of MS which lacks increasing disability and returns to normal between attacks.
c) A relapsing-remitting form of MS where increasing disability occurs during but not between attacks.
d) A secondary, progressive form of MS where increasing disability occurs initially during attacks and is followed later by a steady increase in disability.

5 Figure 19.5 shows a small portion of the retina of the human eye.

a) Identify the receptors X and Y. (2)
b) Which TWO of the numbered nerve fibres will

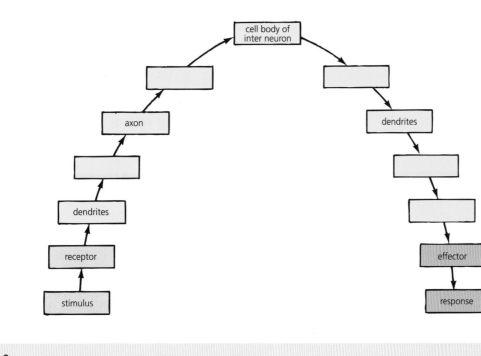

Figure 19.2

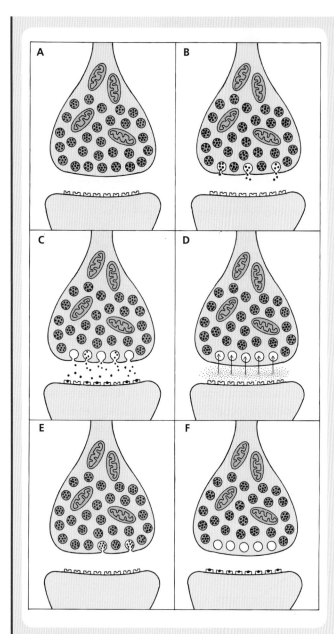

Figure 19.3

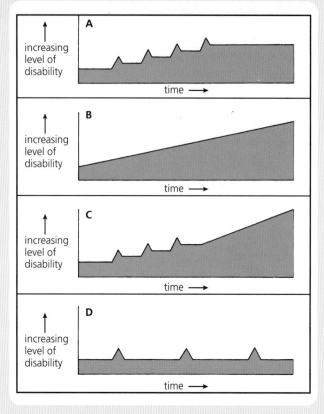

Figure 19.4

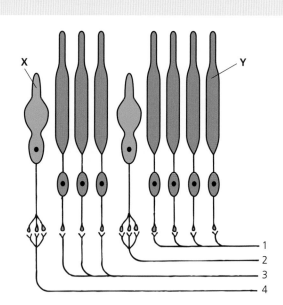

Figure 19.5

transmit an impulse when light of very low intensity reaches the retina? (1)

c) Explain fully your answer to question **b)**. (3)

6 Write notes on the transmission of nerve impulses under the following headings:

a) the synapse (5)

b) diverging pathways (2)

c) converging pathways. (2)

7 An investigation was carried out to see if elevation of pain threshold could be related directly to laughter. A large group of volunteers (male and female) were tested for pain threshold using frozen vacuum wine cooler

sleeves. Each subject indicated when they could no longer stand the pain and then the sleeve was removed. The group was divided into two smaller groups, X and Y. Members of X were shown a documentary video, those of Y, a comedy video. The members of group Y were found to spend much more time laughing than those of group X. The pain threshold of all subjects was then measured again using wine cooler sleeves as before. The results are shown in Figure 19.6.

a) i) By how many units did the mean pain threshold for people shown the documentary video de-crease?

ii) Was this value significantly different from the original value?

iii) Explain your answer to ii). (3)

b) i) By how many units did the mean pain threshold for people shown the comedy video increase?

ii) Was this value significantly different from the original value?

iii) Explain your answer to ii). (3)

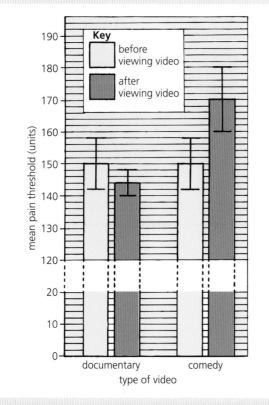

Figure 19.6

c) What conclusion can be drawn from the results of this investigation? (1)

d) Since high levels of endorphins are known to be associated with elevated pain thresholds, it is possible that the physical act of laughing results in release of endorphins. By what means could this hypothesis be tested? (2)

e) In this investigation, it could be argued that changes in pain threshold might be caused by some type of

group effect rather than by comedy. How could this possible source of error be overcome? (1)

8 a) Which lettered curve in the graph in Figure 19.7 represents the activity of a drug that acts as i) an agonist, ii) an antagonist during neurotransmission? (1)

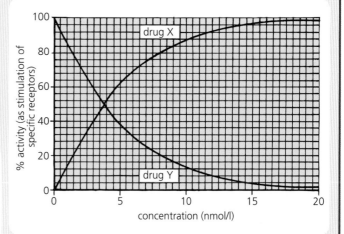

Figure 19.7

b) Explain your choice of answer to a). (2)

c) i) What concentration of drug X in nanomoles per litre (nmol/l) brings about 80% activity?

ii) Express this concentration in moles per litre (mol/l). (2)

d) Suggest why drug Y never fully reaches 0% activity. (2)

9 The human eye is capable of distinguishing between intermittent flashes of light up to a frequency of around 15 hertz. Beyond this point the flashes of light arrive too frequently for the eye to distinguish them individually and therefore they are perceived as a single continuous light. In an investigation to test if alcohol affects reaction time, two 21-year old volunteers (one male, one female) observed a flashing light whose frequency of flashes was increasing at a uniform rate. Each volunteer indicated the frequency at which the flickering light became continuous, by quickly pressing a switch. Five trials were conducted before they consumed alcohol and five trials were conducted 30 minutes after they had consumed a drink containing 80 mg of alcohol. The subjects had not drunk alcohol for 3 days and both had refrained from eating and drinking for 2 hours before the start of the experiment. The results are shown in Table 19.1.

Reaction test trial number	Frequency at which button was pressed (hertz)			
	Female subject		Male subject	
	Before alcohol	After alcohol	Before alcohol	After alcohol
1	15.1	15.6	15.3	16.0
2	14.8	16.5	16.2	17.6
3	14.7	15.8	15.4	**Box Q**
4	16.5	18.4	14.7	15.5
5	15.9	17.7	14.4	15.2
Mean	15.4	**Box P**	15.2	16.2

Table 19.1

a) Calculate the values that should have been included in boxes P and Q. (2)

b) i) What effect did consumption of alcohol have on the frequency at which the button was pressed?

ii) Why does a difference in the particular frequency at which the button is pressed act as an indication of altered reaction time? (3)

c) i) Is it valid to claim from these data that the reaction times of men are less affected by alcohol than those of women?

ii) Explain your answer. (2)

d) i) Explain why the two volunteers were asked to refrain from drinking alcohol for 3 days before the tests.

ii) What THREE features of the experimental procedure were included to try to standardise the quantity of alcohol absorbed before the reaction tests were carried out? (4)

e) i) Identify a feature of the investigation that improved the reliability of the results.

ii) Suggest TWO further features that should be included to increase the reliability of the results in a repeat of the experiment. (3)

10 Distinguish clearly between the members of the following pairs.

a) agonist and antagonist drugs (4)

b) drug sensitisation and drug desensitisation. (5)

20 Communication and social behaviour

1 Figure 20.1 shows a graph of the results from studies of two different types of attachment in human infants.

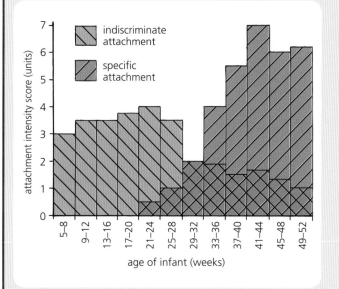

Figure 20.1

a) State the relationship that exists between the two forms of infant attachment as indicated by the graph. (1)

b) i) At what age were the two forms of attachment found to be equal in intensity?

ii) Which form had gained the upper hand 4 weeks later?

iii) Predict the intensity score of indiscriminate attachment at age 2 years.

iv) Why is specific attachment to a primary carer of survival value to an infant? (4)

2 During the Second World War, there were so many homeless infants in some countries that orphanages became overcrowded. In some the babies received little more than food and basic hygiene; in others the staff managed to find time to hold the babies every day and give them a little physical attention. Predict which type of orphanage was found to have the higher infant mortality rate. Suggest why. (2)

3 The accompanying graphs and data refer to experiments involving infant monkeys and cloth and wire 'mothers'. Figures 20.2 and 20.3 give graphs of the results of experiments comparing time spent by infants on different types of 'mother'. Figure 20.4 shows the results from an experiment where the infant monkeys were exposed to a room containing unfamiliar objects.

Their fear score was based on activities such as crying, crouching, rocking and thumb-sucking. A further experiment (called the curiosity test) made use of young monkeys who had been reared from birth in the presence of both cloth and wire 'mothers'. Each monkey was kept in a cage that contained a lever. When this was pressed a window opened for 15 seconds to reveal one of the four views listed in Table 20.1. The number of lever presses scored by a particular view was taken to represent the interest level of the young monkey (see Table 20.1).

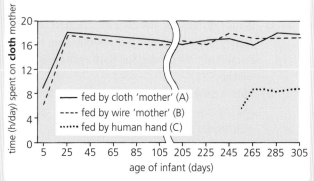

Figure 20.2

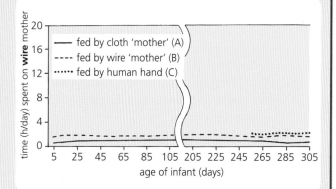

Figure 20.3

View from window	Mean number of lever presses per 4-hour session
Wire 'mother'	602
Live adult monkey	855
Empty chamber	597
Cloth 'mother'	839

Table 20.1

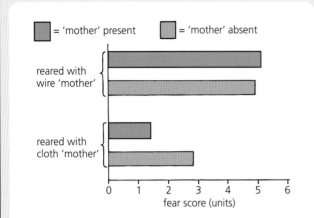

Figure 20.4

a) i) Study Figures 20.2 and 20.3 with respect to the 25-day-old monkeys of group A and state the amount of time per day spent on each type of 'mother'. (1)

ii) Make a generalisation about the type of 'mother' and the time spent by infant monkeys in contact with 'her'. (1)

iii) Is the behaviour that you described in your answer to ii) affected by the infant monkeys' source of food? Explain how you arrived at your answer. (1)

b) i) Which group of monkeys had not known a monkey 'mother' during the first 8 months of their life? (1)

ii) In what way did their behaviour differ from the other groups when they finally met the two types of 'mother'? (1)

c) i) Study Figure 20.4 and identify the type of 'mother' that offered no comfort to a frightened young monkey. (1)

ii) Describe the effect that absence of the cloth 'mother' had on the fear score of an infant exposed to an unfamiliar environment. (1)

iii) Compare your answer to ii) with the fear score of an infant reared with a wire 'mother' and suggest a reason for the difference. (1)

d) With reference to all four views listed in Table 20.1, draw TWO conclusions from the data about the interest level of young monkeys. (2)

4 The statements in the following list were made by parents in response to a survey of types of parental control.

1) *I bribe my child to get her to comply with my wishes.*

2) *I tell my child 'Because I said so' when he asks me why he has to do something.*

3) *I give my child reasons for the expectations that I have for her.*

4) *I frequently explode with anger towards my child.*

5) *I try to help and comfort my child when he is scared or upset or has a problem.*

6) *I frequently encourage my child to talk about her feelings.*

7) *I use withdrawal of affection to punish my child.*

8) *I give in to my child when he throws a tantrum about something.*

9) *I let my child get away with leaving jobs half-finished.*

10) *I respect my child's opinions even if they are different from my own.*

11) *I shout at my child when she misbehaves.*

12) *I just ignore my child's bad behaviour.*

a) Classify the statements under the headings authoritarian (A1), authoritative (A2) and permissive (P) control. (Some statements may belong to more than one category.) (6)

b) Suggest why the division of control into three distinct categories is over-simplistic. (1)

5 Copy and complete Figure 20.5 using the following answers:

- facial expression
- gesture
- invading another's personal space
- pointing a finger
- slumped forward in seat
- tone of voice
- touching
- winking (7)

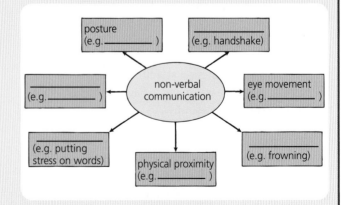

Figure 20.5

6 a) Why are sales staff trained to engage a potential customer in regular eye contact while extolling the virtues of the product on sale? (1)

b) i) State the most common facial expression adopted by sales staff eager for a sale.

ii) Give TWO features of vocal delivery employed by persuasive sales staff. (3)

7 Table 20.2 shows the results from a survey based on a large population of young children.

Age of child (months)	Mean number of words understood
0	0
18	0
24	200
30	600
36	1 050
42	1 400
48	1 650
54	1 900
60	2 150

Table 20.2

a) Draw a line graph of the data. (3)

b) Extract from your graph the age at which a child would, on average, understand 1350 words. (1)

c) What percentage increase in number of words understood occurred between months 30 and 48? (1)

d) At which of the following ages did the rate of understanding of new words occur at the slowest rate? (1)

A 18–24 months   **B** 24–30 months
C 30–36 months   **D** 36–42 months.

e) Based on the trend shown in the graph, predict the number of new words that will be understood by a 6-year old. (1)

8 A large group of students who had never previously met were divided into same-sex pairs, and invited to chat and become acquainted. While they were in conversation with one another, each person's direction of gaze was recorded. This was analysed and the percentage of time that each person spent gazing at the other ('percentage gazing time') was calculated. Figure 20.6 shows an extract from the results obtained for one of the pairs (persons A and B).

a) i) At what time did A's speech come to an end?

ii) At what time did A's percentage gazing time begin to alter, indicating that A was about to stop speaking?

iii) In what way did A's percentage gazing time alter at this stage?

iv) In what way did B's percentage gazing time alter at this stage? (4)

b) Make a generalisation about the difference between the percentage of time spent gazing at the other person while **i)** listening, **ii)** speaking. (2)

9 Discuss the ways in which humans communicate under the headings:

a) non-verbal communication (5)

b) the use of language. (4)

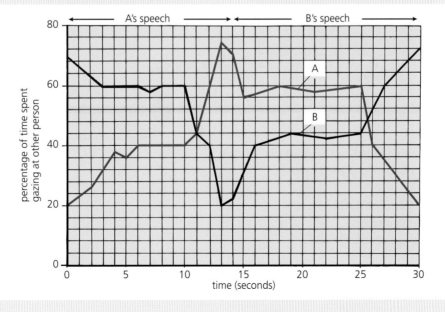

Figure 20.6

10 Figure 20.7 shows a learner using her normal writing hand to do a mirror drawing. This involves joining up the dots to form a star outline while looking only at the mirror image. An investigation was set up to study the effects of two types of practice on this learning process. The 10 members of group A did 20 trials in one day; the 10 members of group B each did one trial daily for 20 days. The graph in Figure 20.8 shows the results.

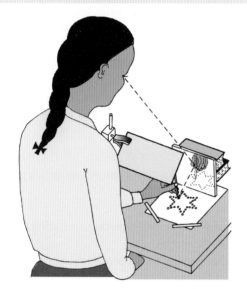

Figure 20.7

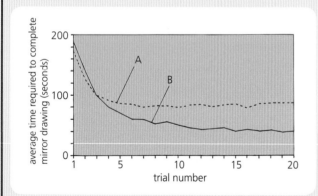

Figure 20.8

a) Which group was being tested for the effect on learning of **i)** distributed practice, **ii)** massed practice? (1)

b) **i)** Compare the effect that the two types of practice had on the learning process.

ii) Give a possible explanation for this difference. (3)

c) Why were as many as 10 learners used in each group? (1)

d) Why is the size of the star outline kept constant throughout the investigation? (1)

e) How could the investigation be adapted to test the effect of an auditory distraction on this learning process? (2)

11 Identical twins volunteered to learn a new task: how to assemble and mount an angled wall bracket for a flat-screen TV. Twin X was given the instruction booklet; twin Y was given a demonstration by an expert.

a) Predict, with reasons, which twin mastered the new task more quickly. (1)

b) Why were identical twins used in this investigation? (1)

12 Imagine that you look after your 5-year-old cousin every Saturday afternoon. One Saturday, annoyed by his failure to persuade you to give him £1 for sweets, he throws a tantrum by screaming and kicking the floor. Some adults might shout at him, others might hug and soothe him. You decide to follow the experts' advice and ignore him.

a) Using the words *extinction, reinforcement* and *reward* in your answer, explain why this course of action is considered to be the best one (although difficult to maintain). (3)

b) If this behaviour is repeated on future Saturdays, why must you be absolutely consistent and not let him have the £1 sometimes 'for an easy life'? (2)

13 In an investigation, a large number of rats learned to select a particular side of a T-maze (see Figure 20.9). Members of group X were rewarded with four food pellets

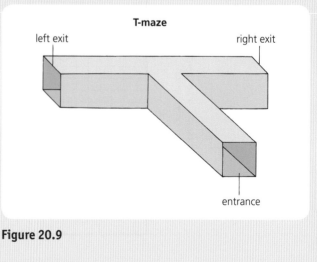

Figure 20.9

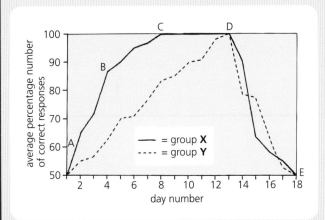

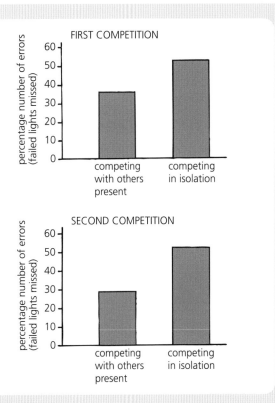

Figure 20.10

and those of group Y with two food pellets for each correct response made. Figure 20.10 shows a graph of the results where each rat ran four trials per day.

a) What name is given to the type of graph indicated by letters A–D? (1)

b) What effect does size of food reward have on the learning process? (1)

c) Suggest why portion C–D of the graph is a straight, flat line. (1)

d) Why does each graph begin at 50% and not 0%? (1)

e) Within each test group of rats, half were trained to choose the right exit and half to choose the left exit. Explain why. (1)

f) i) Between which two letters on the graph does the extinction of learned behaviour occur?

   ii) What change in experimental procedure would account for this extinction of behaviour?

   iii) What conclusion can be drawn about the relationship between resistance to extinction and size of reward during training? (3)

14 A large number of volunteers were given a short period of intensive training to teach them how to monitor light panels for bulbs that failed to light up in the proper sequence. They were then divided into two groups and allowed to compete at this task. The members of one group worked individually but within sight of one another and were able to follow one another's progress. The members of the other group worked individually and in isolation. Each group was then allowed a rest period before the competition was repeated. The bar graphs in Figure 20.5 summarise the results.

a) i) Make a generalisation about the effect on performance of competing with others present compared with competing in isolation.

Figure 20.11

   ii) Which of the following terms is used to refer to this effect? (2)

   A internalisation   B deindividuation

   C group pressure   D social facilitation

b) State the effect on performance of repeating the experiment when:

   i) competing with others

   ii) competing in isolation.

   iii) Give a possible explanation for the effect in each case. (4)

15 The Ku Klux Klan is a secret organisation of white American men who perpetrate acts of violence against black people and other minority groups. The members keep their identities secret and wear robes and hoods to disguise themselves while carrying out their disreputable deeds. Briefly discuss this form of group behaviour including the following terms in your answer: *anonymity, deindividuation, faceless mob, group pressure* and *risk-taking*. (5)

16 Olympic gold medallists in athletics events are a popular choice by manufacturers of expensive sportswear as models to feature in advertising campaigns. Briefly explain how the advertising campaign is intended to work on potential customers. (2)

17 Give an account of human behaviour under the following headings:

a) deindividuation (4)

b) internalisation (3)

c) identification. (2)

Unit **4**

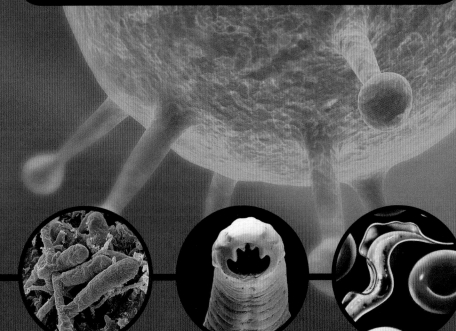

Immunology and Public Health

21 Non-specific defences

1 Figure 21.1 shows a small part of a phagocyte that is approaching a bacterium. Figure 21.2 shows the next five stages in the process of phagocytosis. Arrange them into the correct order. (1)

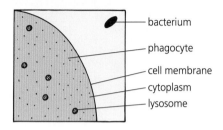

- bacterium
- phagocyte
- cell membrane
- cytoplasm
- lysosome

Figure 21.1

2 Two measurements of white blood cells that are commonly made are:
- a count of the number of each type of white blood cell per microlitre (1×10^{-6} l) of blood
- a calculation of the percentage of each type of white blood cell.

Table 21.1 shows a set of normal values based on a large sample of healthy people. Table 21.2 shows some of the factors responsible for increasing the number and percentage of white cells in the bloodstream.

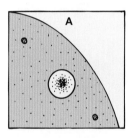

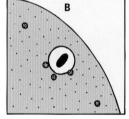

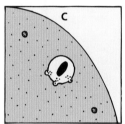

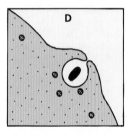

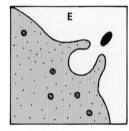

Figure 21.2

Type of white blood cell	White blood cell count	Percentage
Neutrophil	2500–7000	50–70
Eosinophil	100–300	1–3
Monocyte	200–600	4–6
Lymphocyte	1700–3500	25–35

Table 21.1

Type of white blood cell	Factors responsible for increasing number and percentage of white blood cells
Neutrophil	Bacterial infection, rheumatoid arthritis, leukaemia, acute stress
Eosinophil	Allergic reaction, parasitic infection, Hodgkin's disease
Monocyte	Chronic inflammatory disease, parasitic infection, tuberculosis, viral infection
Lymphocyte	Bacterial infection, hepatitis, leukaemia, viral infection

Table 21.2

a) Which of the two ways of measuring white blood cells gives:
   i) an absolute value
   ii) a relative value?
   iii) Explain your answer. (3)

b) How many monocytes would normally be present in a litre of blood? (1)

c) With reference only to the information in Table 21.2, identify:

i) the factor that could cause an increase in number of both monocytes and eosinophils
ii) the factors that affect the neutrophil count but do not affect the others
iii) the types of white blood cell that increase in number in response to leukaemia. (3)

d) Draw a bar chart of the percentage numbers of the white blood cells using mean values. (3)

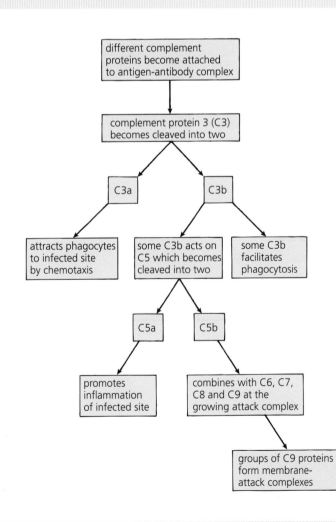

Figure 21.3

3 Read the passage and answer the questions that follow it.

The complement system is a set of antimicrobial proteins present in blood. They remain inactive unless the body becomes infected. They are activated by:

• certain polysaccharides on the surface of bacteria to which the body has not been previously exposed
• antibodies combining with antigens on the surface of an antigen-presenting cell.

In either case a series of events follows where one step leads on to the next one and so on. A simplified version of part of this cascade involving the specific immune system is shown in Figure 21.3. It ends with C9 proteins. These are elongated molecules able to form a ring (that penetrates the cell membrane) called a membrane attack complex (MAC). An MAC encloses a pore of diameter 7–10 nm in the membrane of the antigen-presenting cell, as shown in Figure 21.4.

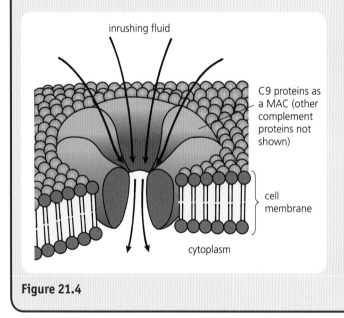
inrushing fluid

C9 proteins as a MAC (other complement proteins not shown)

cell membrane

cytoplasm

Figure 21.4

These pores allow rapid influx of water by osmosis. This results in the swelling up and bursting (lysis) of the cell. Strictly speaking, therefore, it is the complement proteins (and not the antibodies) that directly kill the cell.

a) Referring only to the passage and its accompanying diagrams, identify the word that means:
   i) a series of biochemical events where one leads to the next
   ii) the movement of white blood cells towards a chemical stimulus
   iii) the movement of water molecules from a region of higher water concentration to a region of lower water concentration through a selectively permeable membrane
   iv) a complex carbohydrate. (4)
b) Identify the complement protein that binds to mast cells, triggering the release of histamine. (1)
c) Starting at C9 protein, draw a simple flow chart to show the events that lead to lysis of a bacterium. (4)
d) If a normal pore in the skin is 50 μm in diameter, by how many times is it wider than an MAC pore of diameter 10 nm? (1)

4 Give an account of the inflammatory response. (9)

22 Specific cellular defences

1 a) Rewrite the following sentences, giving only the correct answer from each underlined choice. (5)
   i) People with blood group B have antigen A/B on the surface of their red blood cells.
   ii) People with blood group A would recognise red blood cells bearing antigen B as self/non-self cells.
   iii) People with blood group AB have both/neither anti-A and/nor anti-B antibodies in their plasma.
   iv) People with blood group O can donate blood to people with blood group A, B, AB and O/O only.
   v) People with blood group AB can receive blood from people with blood group A, B, AB and O/AB only.
   b) Copy and complete Table 22.1 using the symbols shown to indicate when agglutination would occur and when it would not occur between potential donors and recipients. (4)

		Blood group of donor			
		A	B	AB	O
Blood group of recipient	A				
	B				
	AB				
	O				

(+ = agglutination; – = no agglutination)

Table 22.1

   c) A person's blood group can be determined by adding a drop of blood to serum containing anti-A antibodies and a second drop of blood to serum containing anti-B antibodies on a slide (see Figure 22.1). The results of testing blood in this way from persons Q, R, S and T are shown in Figure 22.2. State each person's blood group. (4)

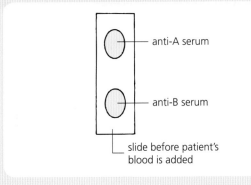

anti-A serum

anti-B serum

slide before patient's blood is added

Figure 22.1

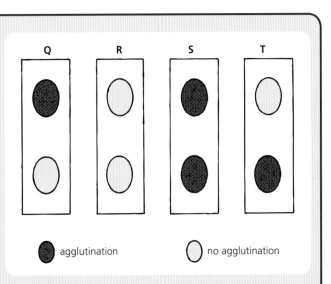

⬤ agglutination   ◯ no agglutination

Figure 22.2

2 A Rhesus negative woman and her Rhesus positive husband produced four children, as shown in Figure 22.3.

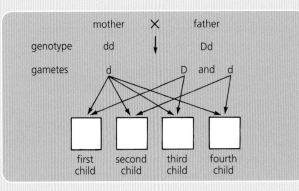

mother × father

genotype   dd   Dd

gametes   d   D and d

first child   second child   third child   fourth child

Figure 22.3

   a) State i) the genotypes, ii) the phenotypes of the four children with respect to the Rhesus factor. (4)
   b) i) Which child would be most likely to suffer haemolytic disease of the newborn?
      ii) Explain why you chose this child and not the other one with the same genotype.
      iii) What treatment could the mother have received to prevent future babies from suffering haemolytic disease?
      iv) If she had not received this treatment, what could be done to try to save the life of a newborn baby suffering haemolytic disease? (6)

3 Figure 22.4 shows a bar chart of results from a survey carried out on 30 000 people to estimate the incidence of asthma in a country. Each bar represents a mean ➜

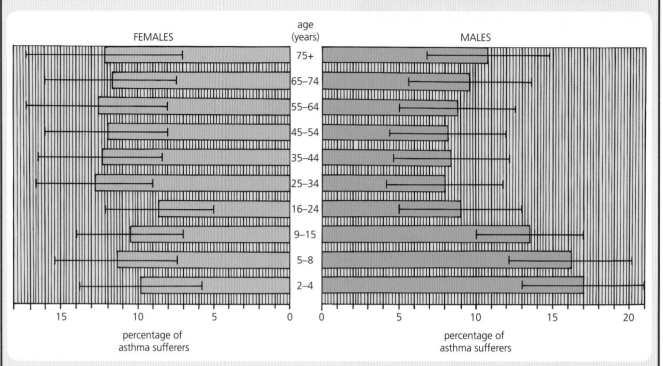

Figure 22.4

value with a 95% confidence level whose range is indicated by error bars.

a) On average, what percentage of
   i)   males aged 55–64 were asthma sufferers
   ii) females aged 35–44 were asthma sufferers? (2)
b) By how many times was the percentage number of male asthma sufferers aged 5–8 greater than that of male sufferers aged 75+? (1)
c) By how many percent was the number of female asthma sufferers aged 25–34 greater than the number of sufferers aged 2–4? (1)
d) At what age was there the least difference in percentage number of asthma sufferers between the two sexes? (1)
e) What general conclusion can be drawn about the percentage number of male sufferers compared with female sufferers in this sample group at age:
   i) 2–15, ii) 25–54? (2)
f) Decide whether each of statements i)–vi) below is true or false and then use T or F to indicate your choice. Where a statement is false, give the data that should have been used in place of that in bold print. (6)
   Based on the information in the bar chart, health care experts could be 95% certain that the number of asthma cases for the whole population would be:
   i)   between **13% and 21%** for 2–4 year-old males

   ii) between **7.2% and 15.2%** for 5–8 year-old females
   iii) between **4.8% and 12.8%** for 25–34 year-old males
   iv) between **8.4% and 16.4%** for 35–44 year-old females
   v)   between **5.0% and 12.6%** for 55–64 year-old males
   vi) between **7.6% and 14.0%** for 65–74 year-old females.

4 Figure 22.5 shows a flow diagram of part of the specific immune response.

   a) Copy the flow diagram and complete it using the boxed answers that follow it. (6)
   b) Add two boxes and arrows to show where 'clone of memory T_C cells' and 'clone of memory B cells' should feature in the diagram. (2)

5 Figure 22.6 shows an antibody complex in action.

   Match labels 1–5 with the following answers. (4)
   A   antibody complex
   B   antigen on surface of bacterium
   C   pathogens inactivated by antibody complex
   D   pathogenic microorganism
   E   receptor site on antibody

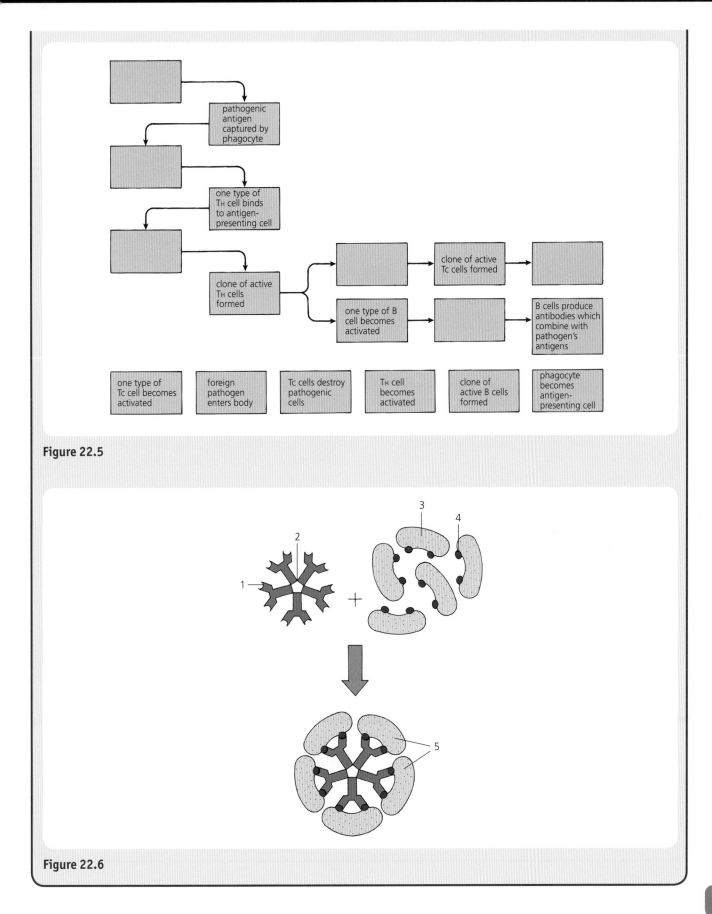

Figure 22.5

Figure 22.6

23 Transmission and control of infectious diseases

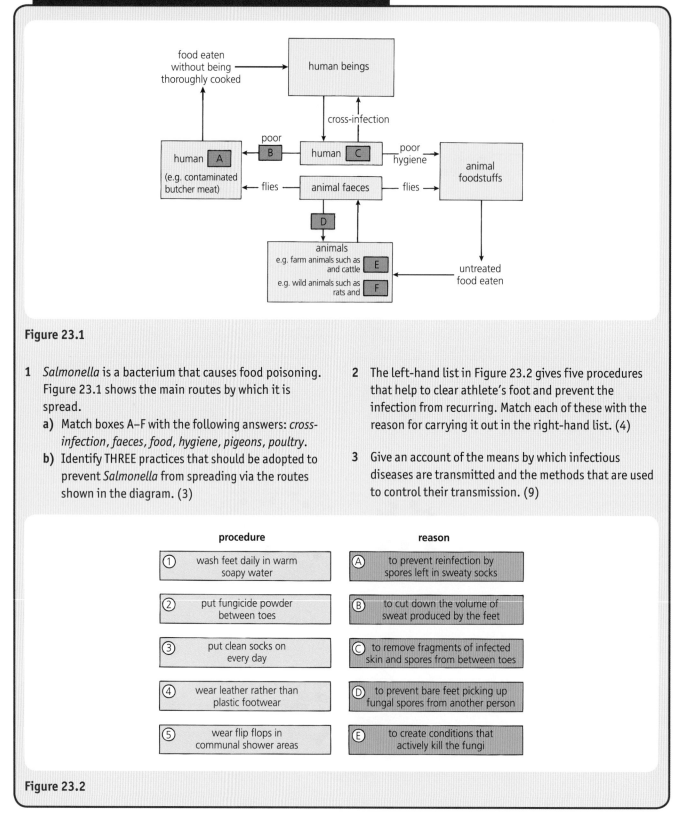

Figure 23.1

1   *Salmonella* is a bacterium that causes food poisoning.
    Figure 23.1 shows the main routes by which it is
    spread.
    a) Match boxes A–F with the following answers: *cross-
       infection, faeces, food, hygiene, pigeons, poultry*.
    b) Identify THREE practices that should be adopted to
       prevent *Salmonella* from spreading via the routes
       shown in the diagram. (3)

2   The left-hand list in Figure 23.2 gives five procedures
    that help to clear athlete's foot and prevent the
    infection from recurring. Match each of these with the
    reason for carrying it out in the right-hand list. (4)

3   Give an account of the means by which infectious
    diseases are transmitted and the methods that are used
    to control their transmission. (9)

procedure

① wash feet daily in warm soapy water

② put fungicide powder between toes

③ put clean socks on every day

④ wear leather rather than plastic footwear

⑤ wear flip flops in communal shower areas

reason

Ⓐ to prevent reinfection by spores left in sweaty socks

Ⓑ to cut down the volume of sweat produced by the feet

Ⓒ to remove fragments of infected skin and spores from between toes

Ⓓ to prevent bare feet picking up fungal spores from another person

Ⓔ to create conditions that actively kill the fungi

Figure 23.2

24 Active immunisation and vaccination and the evasion of specific immune response by pathogens

1 Read the passage and answer the questions that follow it.

Clinical trials of a new drug

A large pharmaceutical company designed a new drug, Q, to treat moderate-to-severe, allergic asthma in sufferers whose condition was barely or inadequately controlled by inhaled corticosteroids. During the development process, the company ran a clinical trial.

Phase I involved trying out drug Q on a small number of healthy volunteers who received financial incentives. In phase II, Q was administered to a large number of unpaid, asthma sufferers who continued to use their inhalers when necessary. Phase III took the form of a placebo-controlled trial involving a very large number of asthma sufferers who continued to inhale corticosteroids as required. Half received drug Q and half received a placebo.

The results of phase III showed that patients treated with Q over a 48-week period suffered significantly fewer asthma attacks and made much less use of their inhalers than the control group. At the end of the trial, 45% of sufferers receiving Q were able to discontinue steroid treatment compared with 7% of the placebo group. The results also indicated that Q was well tolerated and that the frequency of adverse effects was low and similar to that of the control group.

a) Give THREE differences between the phase I and phase II stages of the clinical trial described in the passage. (3)
b) What is the reason for including the control group in phase III? (2)
c) What is the evidence in the passage that drug Q is 'fit for purpose'? (2)
d) i) What is a *placebo*?
   ii) Suggest why 7% of the placebo group were able to discontinue the use of inhaled corticosteroids at the end of the phase III clinical trial. (2)
e) i) In general, would drug Q be better as an addition or an alternative to inhaled corticosteroids for sufferers of allergic asthma?
   ii) Justify your choice of answer. (2)
f) Elderly people consume more than one third of all the drugs prescribed in the UK yet they are normally excluded from phase I of a clinical trial of a new drug. Suggest TWO possible reasons for this apparent discrimination. (2)

2 In some placebo-controlled, clinical trials, the phase III test population is divided at random into three groups, as follows:

- the natural history group **(N)** who receive no treatment of any kind and whose condition is allowed to run its natural course
- the placebo group **(P)** who receive a placebo that convincingly simulates the actual drug but lacks the active ingredient
- the active group **(A)** who receive the drug containing the active ingredient.

Complete the blanks in the following statements using the letters **N**, **P** or **A**.

a) The extent of the placebo effect is indicated by the difference in results between __ and __. (1)
b) The efficacy of the drug's active ingredient is indicated by the difference in results between __ and __. (1)
c) The overall effect of the treatment, the drug and its active ingredient is indicated by the difference in results between __ and __. (1)

3 Table 24.1 shows the immunisation schedule recommended for children in the UK.

a) How many doses of **i)** pertussis vaccine, **ii)** pneumococcal conjugate vaccine would be received by a person who completes the schedule? (2)
b) A child who has completed the full schedule would have received a total of five doses of vaccine against which diseases? (1)
c) Of which vaccine(s) would the same child have received fewest injections? (1)

4 The graphs in Figure 24.1 show the death rates in a European country for two diseases.

a) For which disease did an early drop in death rate occur:
   i) as a result of medical intervention?
   ii) in the absence of medical intervention? (2)
b) Name TWO factors that could account for the decline in death rate from a disease in the absence of medical intervention. (2)
c) i) By how many times was the death rate from tuberculosis greater in 1850 than in 1930?
   ii) Compared with the death rate from diphtheria in 1890, what percentage reduction had occurred by 1920?

→

Age	Vaccine	Number of injections
2 months	Diphtheria + tetanus + pertussis + polio + hib	1
	Pneumococcal conjugate	1
3 months	Diphtheria + tetanus + pertussis + polio + hib	1
	Meningitis C	1
4 months	Diphtheria + tetanus + pertussis + polio + hib	1
	Pneumococcal conjugate	1
	Meningitis C	1
12–13 months	Measles + mumps + rubella	1
	Pneumococcal conjugate	1
	Meningitis C + hib	1
3–5 years	Diphtheria + tetanus + pertussis + polio	1
	Measles + mumps + rubella	1
12–13 years (girls only)	Human papillomavirus (HPV)	3
13–18 years	Diphtheria + tetanus + polio	1

Table 24.1

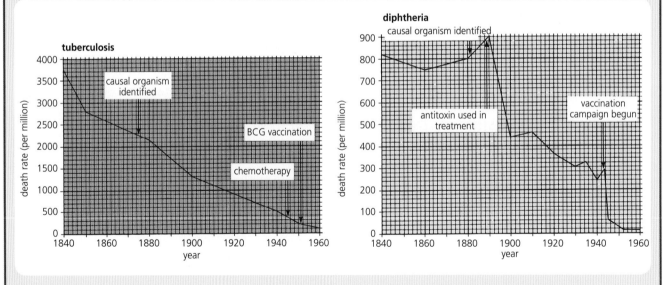

Figure 24.1

iii) In which year did 2 people per 1000 die of tuberculosis?

iv) How many people per 1000 died of diphtheria in 1880? (4)

d) A rise in the number of cases of tuberculosis was recorded during 2009 among homeless people in Britain. Suggest why. (1)

5 Each graph in Figure 24.2 shows the number of reported cases of smallpox in a particular country over a period of time.

a) Which country is:
i) developing?
ii) developed?
iii) Give a reason for your choice of answers. (2)

b) At the start of the vaccination campaign in each country, medical experts suspected that the system of reporting had been inadequate and that many cases had previously gone unreported. In what way do the data in the graphs provide evidence to support this view? (2)

c) i) What was the long-term effect of the vaccination campaign in each case?

ii) Why have scientists been unable, so far, to repeat this success story with a vaccine for malaria? (2)

6 Figure 24.3 shows a graph of the progress of an untreated case of the disease trypanosomiasis caused by protozoa called trypanosomes.

a) i) For how long does each disease cycle last, on average?

ii) How many more trypanosomes per mm³ of blood were present at the end of week 22 compared with the end of week 23? (2)

b) i) By how many variants of *Trypanosoma* was this person affected, as shown by the graph?

ii) Which variant was the most virulent?

iii) What term is used to refer to the fact that a pathogen changes from one genetically distinct form to another? (3)

c) i) During week 25, were the antibodies made by the host more effective during the early part or the later part of the week?

ii) Explain your answer. (2)

7 Read the passage and answer the questions that follow it.

Each influenza virus particle contains a genome composed of eight genes (segments), some of which code for antigenic surface proteins. The three types of influenza virus (A, B and C) that exist differ in the makeup of their genome and in the structure of their surface proteins. Type A infects humans and many other

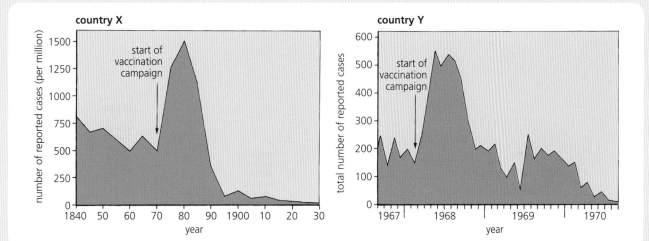

Figure 24.2

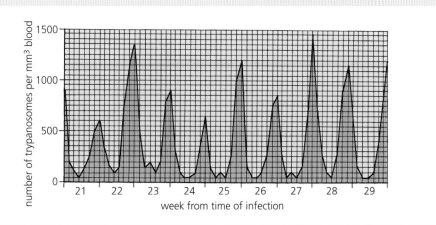

Figure 24.3

animals including pigs, ducks and chickens. Types B and C infect humans but not pigs, ducks or chickens.

Variation in the structure of its surface antigens enables virus type A to evade the host's immune system. This antigenic variation arises in the following two ways:

- by *antigenic drift* resulting from natural mutations that occur continuously and alter the viral genotype
- by *antigenic shift* resulting much less frequently when the genetic material from two different strains of the virus combine to form a new strain.

Figure 24.4 shows an antigenic shift in influenza virus type A that occurred in 1957. A human strain of virus type A and an avian (bird) strain of virus type A infected the same host cell simultaneously. This resulted in the formation of a new variant with a combination of genetic material and surface antigens different from the original strains. The new strain was so successful that it caused a pandemic called Asian flu. Scientists agree that it is only a matter of time until antigenic shift results in the production of another highly virulent strain of influenza with the potential to cause a new pandemic.

a) What is the difference between antigenic shift and antigenic drift? (2)
b) Copy and complete the following paragraph using the answers that follow it. (4)
   A new influenza _____ is needed every year because all the strains of the _____ are continuously undergoing genetic _____ as a result of _____. Therefore one or more _____ strains appear each year able to resist _____ that blocked the _____ by the _____ viral strain.
   (antibodies, drift, infection, mutations, new, previous, vaccine, virus)
c) Choose the answer that correctly completes the following statement. (1)

The new strain of virus formed by antigenic shift differs from the original strain in:
   A genotype only   **B** phenotype only
   C genotype and phenotype. (1)
d) Antigenic drift affects influenza virus types A, B and C but antigenic shift only affects virus type A. Explain why. (2)
e) Using coloured pencils, copy and complete Figure 24.5, which shows how the type A influenza virus that caused the 1968 Hong Kong flu pandemic arose. (3)

8 Give an account of the evasion of specific immune responses by pathogens. (9)

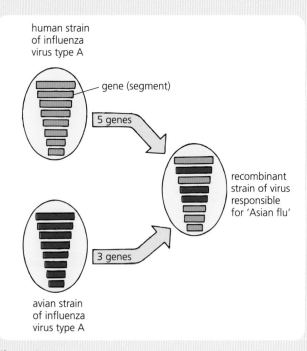

Figure 24.4

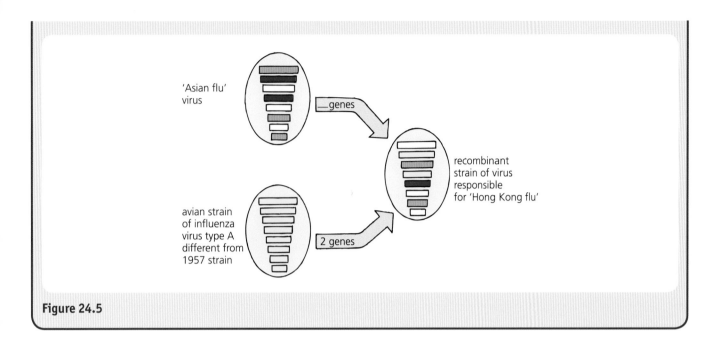

'Asian flu' virus

___ genes

avian strain of influenza virus type A different from 1957 strain

2 genes

recombinant strain of virus responsible for 'Hong Kong flu'

Figure 24.5

Answers

Chapter 1 Division and differentiation in human cells

1 W = zygote, X = embryonic stem cell, Y = tissue (adult) stem cell, Z = specialised cell (3)

2 a) Progenitor (1)

  b) i) B lymphocytes

     ii) Monocytes (2)

  c) 1, 5 (1)

  d) It begins with receptors for SP1 and 2 on its membrane and must receive a signal from SP1 or 2 before it develops receptors for 3, 4 and 5 and so on. (2)

3 a) Nuclear transfer technique (1)

  b) Because she is a genetic copy of another sheep. (1)

  c) i) White

     ii) Because her genetic material came from a white-faced sheep. (2)

  d) i) A

     ii) The DNA that she received came from a sheep not a ram. Therefore she could not have received a Y chromosome necessary to become a male. (2)

4 a) i) B, C, E, G, J

     ii) A, D, F, H, I (2)

  b) ('Open-ended' answer depending on the reader's personal opinion.)

5 a) Jill (1)

  b) i) Unconvincing

     ii) Just because some embryos are lost naturally, this does not justify using embryos for stem cell research. (2)

6 a) i) 8.3

     ii) 6.2 (2)

  b) i) 477 per million

     ii) 0.052% (2)

  c) i) Region A. 2006 is the only year in which the trend is not the same as the country as a whole.

     ii) It shows a much greater overall decrease in lung cancer deaths per 100 000 population. (3)

7 a) See Figure An 1.1. (3)

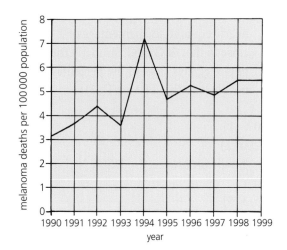

Figure An 1.1

  b) Dependent variable = melanoma death rate; independent variable = time (1)

  c) An increase in number of melanoma deaths per 100 000 population (1)

  d) i) 1994

     ii) Although the trend is upwards, the value for 1994 seems excessively high compared with the others. In addition, no such jump is present in the all Europe data, which otherwise mirror, at a lower level, the data of the northern European country. (3)

  e) 55 (1)

  f) i) 37.5

     ii) 8% (2)

  g) i) B

     ii) Although the overall trend is upwards, the values fluctuate slightly so the next value is more likely to be the slightly lower one than one that varies greatly from the previous value. (2)

  h) More precautions taken; earlier diagnosis (2)

8 See core text pages 3, 9–10. (9)

Chapter 2   Structure and replication of DNA

1 a) X = 22.0 Y = 0.98 (2)

  b) i) The number of adenine bases in DNA equals the number of thymine bases and the number of guanine bases equals the number of cytosine bases (A:T =1:1 and G:C = 1:1).

    ii) Yes

    iii) Because the percentage of A is always very nearly equal to the percentage of T but not close to that of G or C. Similarly the percentage of G is always close to the percentage of C but not close to that of A or T. (3)

  c) C (1)

2 a) 30% (1)

  b) 3200 (1)

3 a) i) 1 = chromosome; 2 = DNA; 3 = base

    ii) 1

    iii) 3 (5)

  b) i) 10 000:1

    ii) Because this is a constant, reliable measurement whereas length measured in μm varies according to degree of coiling. (2)

4 a) When the DNA strands become reunited, some containing ^{14}N pair with others containing ^{14}N, some ^{14}N combine with ^{15}N and some ^{15}N combine with ^{15}N. This produces three distinct marker bands. (2)

  b) When the DNA strands become reunited, those of virus 1 are not complementary to those of virus 2 so no 'hybrid' $^{14}N + ^{15}N$ DNA double helices can be formed. (2)

  c) *E. coli* host cells could be grown in ^{15}N as their only source of nitrogen for many generations. They could then be infected with bacteriophage viruses that would take up ^{15}N in the copies that they made of themselves. (3)

5 a) See Figure An 2.1. (6)

  b) i) 20 000 minutes

    ii) During replication, many replication forks operate simultaneously, which ensures speedy copying of the DNA. (2)

6 See core text pages 24, 29–31. (9)

Chapter 3   Gene expression

1 a) 2

  b) 4

  c) 1

  d) 3 (3)

2 a) 1 = C, 2 = T, 3 = T, 4 = A, 5 = U, 6 = A, 7 = G, 8 = C, 9 = G (2)

  b) P = transcription and release of mRNA. Q = translation of mRNA into protein. (1)

  c) See Table An 3.1. (2)

Amino acid	Codon	Anticodon
Alanine	GCG	CGC
Arginine	CGC	GCG
Cysteine	UGU	ACA
Glutamic acid	GAA	CUU
Glutamine	CAA	GUU
Glycine	GGC	CCG
Isoleucine	AUA	UAU
Leucine	CUU	GAA
Proline	CCG	GGC
Threonine	ACA	UGU
Tyrosine	UAU	AUA
Valine	GUU	CAA

Table An 3.1

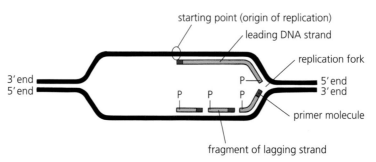

Figure An 2.1

d) CAA (1)

e) U = proline, V = glutamine, W = glutamic acid, X = cysteine, Y = arginine, Z = isoleucine (2)

f) **i)** ACACUUGCGGGC

ii) TGTGAACGCCCG (2)

3 a) Casein contains them all. Group 2 rats gained weight throughout the experiment. Zein lacks two essential amino acids. Group 1 rats lost weight throughout the experiment. (4)

b) **i)** Zein

ii) Their diet could have been changed to casein or to zein supplemented with the two essential amino acids that it lacks. (3)

c) 35 g (1)

d) 20% (1)

4 See core text pages 38–41. (9)

Chapter 4   Genes and proteins in health and disease

1 See Figure An 4.1. (1)

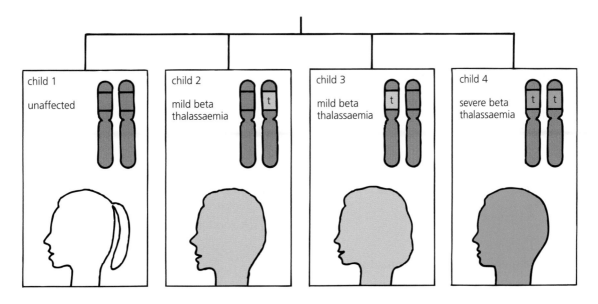

N — AAp — AAm — AAf — AAm — AAs — AAd — AAe — AAe — AAf — AAj

Figure An 4.1

2 a) **i)** Lower molecular weight

ii) This is suggested by the fact that they have travelled the greatest distance from the negative electrode. (2)

b) **i)** Alpha-2-globulins

ii) Iron-deficiency anaemia (2)

c) **i)** D

ii) Because gamma-globulins also increase in concentration for other reasons such as response to viral invasion. (2)

3 a) **i)** Mutations (%)

ii) Dosage of X-rays (2)

b) As the dosage of X-rays increases so does the percentage of mutations. (1)

c) **i)** C

ii) B (2)

d) 0.1 per million cells (1)

4 a) Deletion (1)

b) Substitution (1)

c) Insertion (1)

5 See Figure An 4.2. (4)

6 a) The mutated gene is no longer able to code the correct message for the production of its particular enzyme. Lack of the enzyme prevents the pathway from proceeding normally. (2)

b) **i)** Q

ii) R

iii) T (3)

c) **i)** All the excess phenylalanine has been converted to tyrosine.

ii) The PKU sufferer is unable to make the enzyme needed to convert phenylalanine to tyrosine.

child 1 — unaffected

child 2 — mild beta thalassaemia — t

child 3 — mild beta thalassaemia — t

child 4 — severe beta thalassaemia — t t

Figure An 4.2

iii) The tyrosine has been converted to other metabolites. (3)

7 a) i) Trinucleotide repeat expansion
      ii) Single-gene mutation (2)
    b) See Table An 4.1. (3)

Feature	Huntington's disease	Fragile X syndrome
Chromosome affected	4	X
Codon repeated	CAG	CGG
Number of repeats normally needed to cause disorder	36	230

Table An 4.1

    c) i) Earlier onset of the disease and faster progression of it than in previous generations.
      ii) Further CAG codons have been added at each generation. (3)

8 a) Cell 1 = deletion; cell 2 = duplication (2)
    b) i) Cell 1
      ii) Essential genes would probably have been lost. (2)

9 See core text pages 52–55. (9)

Chapter 5   Human genomics

1 AACCGATCAGCGCAGCGCTTGATCAGATCGC GCTAG (1)

2 a) No (1)
    b) These SNPs might both be neutral mutations that have no effect on the protein that is coded. (1)

3 a) i) It is a variation in DNA sequence that affects a single base pair in a DNA chain.
      ii) Site 4 (2)
    b) 5 (1)
    c) i) 7 and 12
      ii) 5 and 9
      iii) 8 (3)
    d 17 (1)
    e) i) CTTATG
      ii) 45% (2)
    f) 10 (1)
    g) 4 and 11 (1)
    h) Increase the number of people sampled and include more sites in the study. (2)

4 a) i) 10^7 m
      ii) 10^4 km; ten thousand kilometres (2)

    b) i) No
      ii) It is based on the genomes of several people. (2)

5 a) See Table An 5.1. (4)

Alleles of gene present in genome	State of enzyme	Person's metabolic profile
Two null alleles	Non-functional	Poor
One null allele and one inferior allele	Partly functional	Intermediate
One or two normal alleles	Fully functional	Extensive
More than two copies of normal allele	Highly functional	Ultra-rapid

Table An 5.1

    b) Duplication (1)
    c) i) Poor metabolisers
      ii) Their bodies will be so slow to clear the drug that it may do them harm. (2)
    d) i) Ultra-rapid metabolisers
      ii) Their bodies would remove the drug so quickly that it would not have time to bring about the desired effect. (2)
    e) If the personal genome sequencing becomes routine then knowledge of a person's DNA profile may enable doctors to customise medical treatments to suit an individual's exact requirements. (2)

6 a) R and V (1)
    b) Q and T (1)
    c) i) Yes
      ii) They have 50% of their DNA bands in common with the parents of P. (2)
    d) i) No
      ii) They have no DNA bands in common with R and V. (2)

7 a) See core text pages 63, 66, 68. (4)
    b) See core text page 69. (3)
    c) See core text page 70. (2)

Chapter 6   Metabolic pathways

1 a) i) 5
     ii) 3 (2)
   b) Some of I would be converted to G by enzyme 5 and then G would be converted to H by enzyme 4. (2)
   c) i) H could become L and M by the action of enzyme 8 and then L and M could become J and K by the action of enzyme 7.
     ii) H + I $\xrightarrow{enzyme6}$ J + K $\xrightarrow{enzyme7}$ L + M
     iii)G $\xrightarrow{enzyme4}$ H $\xrightarrow{enzyme8}$ L + M $\xrightarrow{enzyme7}$ J + K $\xrightarrow{enzyme6}$ H + I (3)
   d) It allows finely tuned control and prevents build-ups and bottlenecks. (1)
2 a) P and S (1)
   b) i) Q, S, P, R
     ii) R, P, S, Q (2)
   c) B (1)
3 a) i) Concentration of substrate
     ii) Independent
     iii)It caused an increase in reaction rate. (3)
   b) Concentration of enzyme (1)
   c) i) A
     ii) C
     iii)B (3)
   d) More enzyme could be added. (1)
4 a) i), ii) and iii) See Figure An 6.1. (4)
   b) A (1)
   c) 3 times (1)
   d) i) 61.54%
     ii) 10% (2)

e) There would always be a few enzyme sites blocked by inhibitor. (1)
5 a) i) Y
     ii) Z
     iii)X (2)
   b) X (1)
   c) X, Y and Z (1)
   d) Non-competitive (1)
6 a) 1, 2 and 3 (1)
   b) Substrate concentration (1)
   c) 4, 5 and 6 (1)
   d) Experiment = 4, 5 and 6; controls = 1, 2 and 3 (2)
   e) i) Iodine solution
     ii) Non-competitively
     iii)If it had been a competitive inhibitor, the inhibitory effect would have decreased as substrate concentration increased and this would have resulted in some yellow colour appearing in tube 6 and maybe a faint yellow colour in tube 5. However, iodine completely inhibited the enzyme at all concentrations of ONPG showing that it acted non-competitively. (4)
7 a) i) Carbamyl phosphate and aspartate
     ii) Carbamyl aspartate and phosphate
     iii)Cytidylic acid (3)
   b) i) The concentration of carbamyl phosphate will increase.
     ii) Fewer molecules of P will be free to act on carbamyl phosphate. (2)
   c) i) Decreased

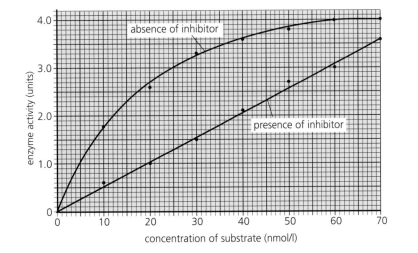

Figure An 6.1

ii) There will be so little cytidylic acid present that very few molecules of enzyme P will be affected by the negative feedback process. (2)

d) All 3 (1)

Chapter 7   Cellular respiration

1 a) and **b)** See Figure An 7.1. (4)

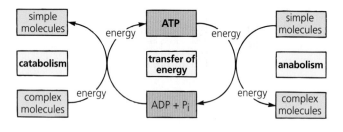

Figure An 7.1

c) i) C

ii) A

iii) C

iv) A (4)

2 a) 56% (1)

b) 1267.2 kJ (1)

c) Synthesis of protein from amino acids; contraction of muscles (2)

3 a) See Table An 7.1. (5)

Stage of respiratory pathway	Principal reaction or process that occurs	Products
Glycolysis	Splitting of glucose into [pyruvate]	[ATP], NADH and pyruvate
[Citric] acid cycle	Removal of [hydrogen] ions from molecules of respiratory [substrate]	[CO_2], $FADH_2$, [NADH] and ATP
[Electron] transport chain	Release of [energy] to form ATP	ATP and [water]

Table An 7.1

b) Glycolysis (1)

c) Electron transport chain (1)

d) Glycolysis and citric acid cycle (2)

e) Citric acid cycle and electron transport chain (2)

4 a) i) Intermembrane space

ii) A flow of high-energy electrons from NADH and $FADH_2$ pumps H ions across

the membrane against a concentration gradient. (3)

b) i) ATP synthase

ii) The return flow of H$^+$ ions to the region of lower H$^+$ ion concentration via molecule X makes part of it rotate and catalyse the synthesis of ATP. (3)

c) By stopping electron flow, cyanide brings the movement of H$^+$ ions to a halt therefore no ATP is synthesised and the organism lacks access to energy and dies. (2)

5 a) See Figure An 7.2. (4)

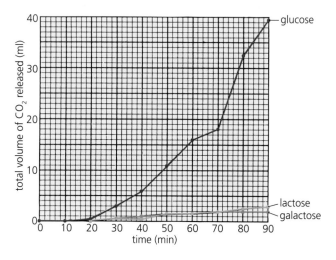

Figure An 7.2

b) i) The result at 70 min

ii) It is much lower than would be expected from the general trend. (2)

c) 6400% (1)

d) It is able to make very good use of glucose but not able to make good use of galactose or lactose. (1)

e) i) It is hardly able to break lactose down.

ii) If it had been able to do so, glucose would have been released from lactose and rapidly used as a respiratory substrate. (2)

f) Repeat the experiment. (1)

g) It would have digested lactose to glucose and galactose and therefore the lactose flask would have worked as well as the original flask containing glucose. There would have been no effect in the galactose flask. The flask containing glucose would work as well as, but no better than, before. (2)

6 a) D (1)

b) B (1)

c) i) Yes
   ii) Because excess carbohydrate can follow route IDB or IKMEB to fat. (3)
d) They can break down stores of fat (and eventually tissue protein) to obtain energy after they have exhausted their supply of glycogen. (2)
7 See core text pages 101–105. (9)

Chapter 8   Energy systems in muscle cells

1 a) See Figure An 8.1. (3)
  b) The longer the event, the larger the volume of oxygen breathed in. The longer the event, the greater the percentage of energy obtained from aerobic respiration. The longer the event, the more energy expended. (3)
  c) i) Event 1 = 2 kJ/m; event 5 = 0.33 kJ/m
     ii) 6 times (3)
2 a) i) 1.08 mg/cm^3
     ii) 12.18 and 12.45 (2)
  b) i) B
     ii) The start of the steep rise in lactic acid concentration that occurs at this time indicates anaerobic respiration occurring during intensive exercise. (2)
  c) i) 5.5 times
     ii) A
     iii) 66.67% (3)
3 a) See core text pages 113–114. (3)
  b) See core text pages 114–116. (6)

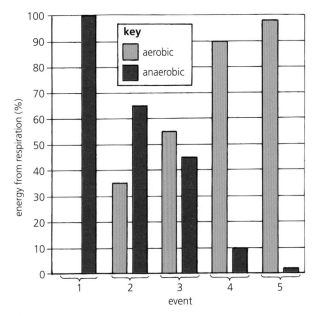

Figure An 8.1

Chapter 9   The structure and function of reproductive organs and gametes and their role in fertilisation and Chapter 10   Hormonal control of reproduction

1 a) D, A, E, C, B (1)
  b) i) D, A and E
     ii) Ovulation
     iii) LH
     iv) Pituitary gland (4)
  c) i) Corpus luteum
     ii) Progesterone and oestrogen
     iii) Inhibitory effect (preventing release of LH) (4)
2 a) See Figure An 9.1. (3)

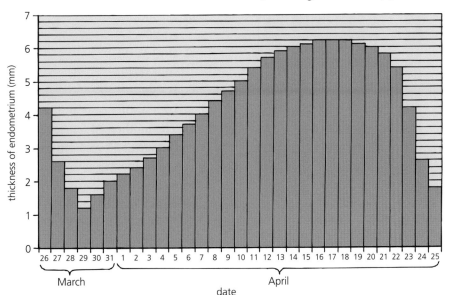

Figure An 9.1

b) 22, 23, 24 (1)

c) 8 April (1)

d) i) high

   ii) low

   iii) high

   iv) low (4)

3 a) V = seminiferous tubule, W = blood capillary, X = interstitial cell, Y = germline cell, Z = sperm (5)

b) X (1)

c) ICSH (interstitial cell-stimulating hormone) (1)

d) It is exerted by negative feedback control. As the concentration of testosterone builds up in the bloodstream, it reaches a level where it inhibits the secretion of FSH and ICSH by the pituitary gland. This leads in turn to a decrease in testosterone concentration, which is soon followed by resumption of activity of the pituitary gland and so on. (3)

4 a) See core text page 131. (4)

b) See core text pages 131–2. (5)

Chapter 11   Biology of controlling fertility

1 a) See Figure An 11.1. (3)

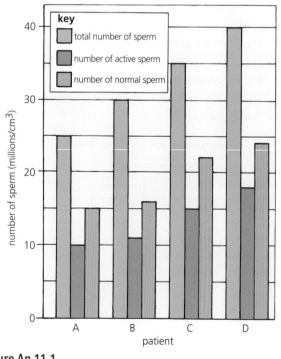

number of sperm (millions/cm³)

key
- total number of sperm
- number of active sperm
- number of normal sperm

patient

Figure An 11.1

b) B (1)

2 a) Sperm are unable to leave the man's body since both of his sperm ducts have been cut and tied. (1)

b) Compared with younger men, middle-aged men are more likely to already have a family and not wish to father any more children. (1)

3 These questions are intended to stimulate debate. There are no 'correct' answers to them.

4 A = 3, B = 2, C = 5, D = 6, E = 4, F = 1 (5)

5 See core text pages 134–137. (9)

Chapter 12   Ante- and postnatal screening

1 a) 5′-nucleotidase and alkaline phosphatase (1)

b) Bilirubin, albumin and GGT (1)

c) In a normal pregnancy they remain unaltered, so if they rise this indicates a problem. (1)

d) i) Serum bile acids

   ii) Alkaline phosphatase

   iii) Alkaline phosphatase level rises during a normal pregnancy therefore a rise may not be indicating a problem. The level of serum bile acids does not rise normally, so it does indicate a problem. (3)

e) To ensure that the level of bile serum acids is not artificially elevated following the absorption of digested food into the bloodstream. (1)

2 a) Down's syndrome (1)

b) i) 32%

   ii) 4% (2)

c) i) 4%

   ii) 28% (2)

d) i) 3 MoM

   ii) 30% (2)

e) i) 2 MoM

   ii) 24% (2)

f) i) No

   ii) 8% still occur at this level of MoM. (2)

3 a) The mothers of fetuses 2 and 5 are not over the age of 35 yet both had a fetus with Down's syndrome. (1)

b) 6 (1)

c) 10 (1)

d) 77.78% (1)

4 a) i) Hh

   ii) hh (2)

b) i) Neither is old enough yet to show a

phenotypic expression of the disorder which would indicate the presence of the H allele in their genotype.

   ii) A = 3 in 4, B = 1 in 2, C = 1 in 2, D = no chance (5)

5 **a)** 2, 6 and 10 (1)

 b) 1 in 2 chance (1)

 c) i) 1 in 4

   ii) 1 in 2 (2)

6 See core text pages 143–148. (9)

Chapter 13 The structure and function of arteries, capillaries and veins

1 **a)** Pulmonary vein, left atrium, left ventricle, aorta, renal artery (5)

 b) Jugular vein, vena cava, right atrium, right ventricle, pulmonary artery (5)

2 **a) and b)** See Figure An 13.1. (8)

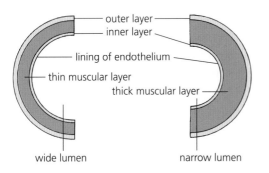

Figure An 13.1

 c) i) Veins possess valves whereas arteries do not.

   ii) They prevent backflow of blood. See Figure An 13.2. (4)

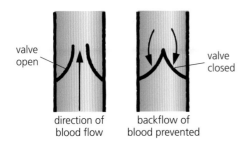

Figure An 13.2

3 Capillary → venule → vein → artery → arteriole → capillary → venule → vein → artery → arteriole → capillary (4)

4 **a) i)** Increase

   ii) Decrease

   iii) The skeletal muscle is working hard and needs plenty of glucose and oxygen which are supplied by the bloodstream. Absorption of digested food is less important during strenuous exercise. (4)

 b) i) Skin

   ii) Kidneys (2)

 c) i) Brain

   ii) The energy demand by brain cells is continuous and steady regardless of the level of activity occurring elsewhere in the body. (2)

 d) Vasoconstriction reduces blood flow to a body part because muscles in the walls of the arterioles supplying the body part contract making the bore of the tubes become narrow; vasodilation has the opposite effect. (2)

5 **a)** D (1)

 b) D (1)

 c) A (1)

 d) C (1)

6 **a)** 1 = vein, 2 = artery, 3 = venule, 4 = arteriole, 5 = capillary (5)

 b) Higher at W, lower at X (1)

 c) i) Tissue fluid

   ii) When blood arrives in a capillary bed it undergoes pressure filtration and plasma is squeezed out of the vessels. This liquid bathing the cells is called tissue fluid.

   iii) It supplies them with dissolved oxygen, useful ions and soluble food molecules.

   iv) Tissue fluid contains little or no protein. (4)

 d) Z = lymphatic vessel. It absorbs tissue fluid (now called lymph) and returns it to the blood circulatory system via the lymphatic system. (2)

 e) D (1)

7 **a)** CO = HR × SV (1)

 b) i) 5.76 l/min

   ii) 100 beats/min

   iii) 100 ml

   iv) 120 ml (4)

 c) Person iv) is fitter. The larger stroke volume indicates that their heart muscle is more powerful. (2)

8 See core text pages 164–165. (9)

Chapter 14 Structure and function of the heart

1 a) i)   Right = 26 mm Hg, left = 120 mm Hg
      ii) The wall of the left ventricle is thicker than that of the right ventricle. This enables the left ventricle to exert the higher pressure needed to pump blood all round the body. (2)
    b) i)   0 mm Hg
      ii) 80 mm Hg
      iii) 20 mm Hg
      iv) 10 mm Hg (4)
    c) 0.1 s (1)
    d) 0.15–0.4 s (1)
    e) During diastole the pressure of blood in the pulmonary artery returns to 16 mm Hg where it started. (1)

2 1 = increases, 2 = open, 3 = aorta, 4 = stretched, 5 = reservoir, 6 = relax, 7 = decreases, 8 = shut, 9 = recoil, 10 = body (9)

3 a) i)   Z
      ii) X
      iii) Y (2)
    b) i)   B
      ii) A
      iii) B's waves are further apart than normal but remain coordinated whereas A's waves are uncoordinated. (4)

4 a) See Table An 14.1. (6)

Part of circulatory system	Blood pressure (mmHg)	Drop in pressure in this part of system (mmHg)
Left ventricle	100	0
Aorta	100	0
Large arteries	95–100	5
Small arteries	85–95	10
Arterioles	35–85	50
Capillaries	15–35	20
Venules	6–15	9
Small veins	2–6	4
Large veins	1–2	1
Venae cavae	0–1	1

Table An 14.1

    b) i) Arterioles and capillaries
      ii) 70 mm Hg
      iii) The blood vessels offer resistance to blood flow, which contributes to the drop in pressure. (3)

5 a) See core text page 169. (5)
    b) See core text pages 170–171. (4)

Chapter 15 Pathology of cardiovascular disease

1 Men always suffer a higher death rate than women. The death rate increases with age. The death rates are all decreasing with time. (3)

2 1 mmol/l = 386.6 mg/l
   1 mmol/l = 38.66 mg/dl
   1.56 mmol/l = 1.56 × 38.66 mg/dl
   = 60.31 mg/dl (desirable level of HDL-cholesterol)
   3.88 mmol/l = 3.88 × 38.66 mg/dl
   = 150 mg/dl (borderline level of LDL-cholesterol) (3)

3 a) 20 mg (1)
    b) 0.75 mmol/l (1)
    c) i)   20 mg
      ii) 80 mg (2)
    d) H (1)
    e) E and H (1)
    f) i)   E
      ii) It produces the greatest decrease in LDL-cholesterol at the lowest concentration of dose. (2)

4 The greater the decrease in level of LDL-cholesterol, the greater the expected percentage decrease in incidence of CVD. The older the patient, the lower the expected percentage decrease in incidence of CVD. (2)

5 a) i)   U
      ii) N (2)
    b) i)   M = Hh, affected
      ii) X = hh, unaffected (2)
    c) i)   S
      ii) Genotype could be HH or Hh (2)
    d) i)   1 in 2
      ii) 1 in 2 (2)
    e) Person V has inherited the condition from his father, person P. This would not be possible if the trait were sex-linked. (1)

Chapter 16 Blood glucose levels and obesity

1 a) See Figure An 16.1. (3)

b) The diagram has been drawn as two interrelated circuits to show that a **physiological** factor under **homeostatic** control is constantly wavering on either side of its **normal** value. When it **deviates** from the norm, it is returned to this value by negative **feedback** control. If it overshoots the mark, a **reverse** set of mechanisms is triggered which returns the factor to its norm. If it now overshoots the mark in the opposite direction, the opposite set of **responses** is made and so on. (6)

2 a) i) Between 07.00 and 08.00
   ii) Homeostasis (2)

b) i) 08.00
   ii) They both increased.
   iii) Time is needed for glucose in the blood to reach the pancreas and for the receptor cells to respond and release more insulin. (4)

c) i) Suppresses
   ii) The concentration of fatty acids drops. If insulin promoted the breakdown of fat, the concentration of fatty acids would increase. (2)

d) i) See Figure An 16.2.

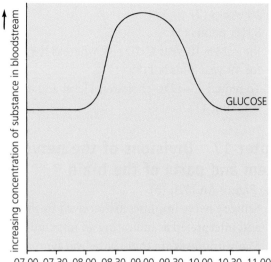

Figure An 16.2

   ii) After ingestion of glucose the maximum value of blood glucose concentration reached would be much higher. The blood glucose level would have only shown a slight decrease by 11.00 hours. (4)

e) The babies of diabetic mothers receive more glucose (which promotes weight gain). Their mother's blood is rich in glucose because she produces insufficient insulin to store her excess glucose as glycogen. (1)

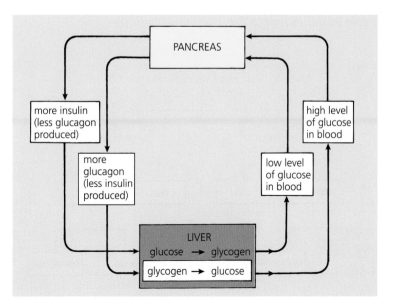

Figure An 16.1

3 **i)** 25 weeks

   ii) 10 weeks (2)

4 **a)** 8 risk points (1)

   b) Joe = 18% 10-year CHD risk whereas the average for 49-year-olds is 11%. (1)

   c) To reduce his LDL-cholesterol level and to stop smoking. (1)

Chapter 17 Divisions of the nervous system and parts of the brain

1 See Figure An 17.1. (5)

2 **a)** Sensory nerve impulses are received by the brain and interpreted as indicating an impending crisis. Many impulses are transmitted via sympathetic nerves to certain parts of the body. This results in preparations being made for 'fight or flight' such as increased heart rate and dilation of air passages. Extra energy becomes available to cope with the crisis. After the crisis, many impulses are transmitted via the parasympathetic nerves. This results in decreased heart rate, constriction of air passages and increased rate of peristalsis as the body calms down. (4)

   b) It is possible that they would sink into a coma. (1)

3 **a)** **i)** The muscle will contract.

      ii) It will decrease.

      iii) Less blood will flow to the gut allowing more to be diverted to skeletal muscles where it is needed. (3)

   b) **i)** They will make the muscle contract and close the sphincter valves.

      ii) Parasympathetic nerve impulses sent to the same muscles.

iii) It would be of advantage when the body is at rest and digesting a meal because it would enable the sphincters to open and allow food to pass through. (4)

4 **a)** **i)** See Figure An 17.2.

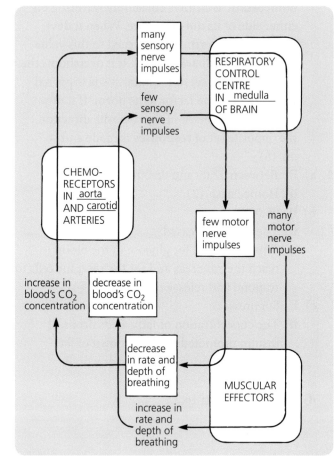

Figure An 17.2

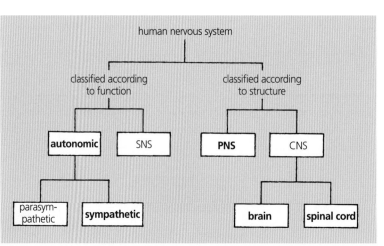

Figure An 17.1

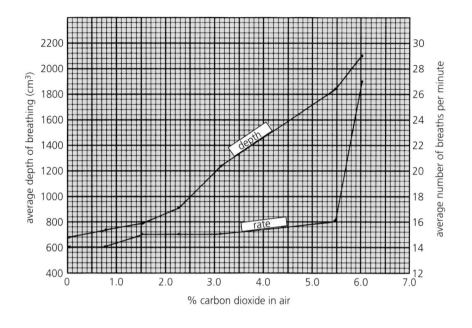

Figure An 17.3

ii) It maintains the body's internal environment within certain tolerable limits. (8)

b) i) See Figure An 17.3.

ii) Percentage carbon dioxide in inspired air

iii) As percentage carbon dioxide in inspired air increases, rate and depth of breathing increase.

iv) Depth (7)

5 a) Taste and touch (2)

b) The leg has few sensory receptors relative to its actual size. (1)

c) D (1)

d) A (1)

e) X = foot, Y = brow, Z = lips (2)

f) The ears would be much larger because a cat's ears are much more mobile than those of a human. (2)

6 a) A. The right side of the object becomes an image on the left side of the brain where the speech motor area is located. (2)

b) D. The left side of the object becomes an image on the right side of the brain which also controls movement of the left hand. (2)

7 a) 3 and 5 (2)

b) i) Reading a book silently

ii) Reading a book out loud (2)

c) 3 → 4 → 1 → 2 (1)

d) i) No effect

ii) The person would be unable to speak. (2)

8 a) It denies the nerve cells a supply of oxygen. Therefore they become damaged and some die. (1)

b) i) Left

ii) The left side of the brain controls the right side of the body. (2)

c) To establish the state of the brain at the start so that it could be compared with its state after the training period. (1)

d) Figure 14.4 shows the motor region of the cerebrum. The part of it responsible for sending motor messages to the hand corresponds to the orange area in Figure 14.8. It has been picked up by the fMRI because it is active and sending messages to the hand. (2)

e) The exercise brought about an increase in brain function. (1)

f) i) The brain was able to retain this regained function after 4 weeks.

ii) The orange area is still active after 4 weeks and bigger than before. (2)

g) i) They only used five people who were all men and all right-handed.

ii) Use many more than five people and extend the investigation to include women and left-handed people. (6)

Chapter 18   Perception and memory

1 B (1)

2 **a)** To increase the reliability of the results. (1)

   b) To prevent a gender bias. (1)

   c) So that their behaviour would be independent of, and not be influenced by, that of any other baby. (1)

   d) Temperature, lighting and time of day (3)

   e) On average, they are unable to crawl until they reach 6 months. (1)

   f) **i)** Yes

      ii) It is unlikely that the babies would have met clues and learned about depth perception during their first 6 months of life. (2)

3 **a)** A = 4, B = 5, C = 2, D = 3, E = 6, F = 1 (5)

   b) Divide a large group of hungry volunteers into two smaller groups A and B. Keep the members of group A hungry but give those in group B a satisfying meal. Show all the volunteers Figure 18.5 and find out if a significantly larger number of group A see an image of food (rather than a face) compared with the members of group B. (3)

4 Four digits can be arranged into a large enough number of combinations to make each PIN number different from the others yet at the same time be short enough to be easily remembered. (2)

5 Person **b)** will be faster because they will be familiar with the first four codes that will act as chunks. They will only need to memorise the last four digits. Person **a)** is confronted with 14 unfamiliar digits. (2)

6 **a)** To prevent them from rehearsing the letters that they will be asked to recall. (1)

   b) **i)** 35

      ii) 4 (2)

   c) They would be allowed to rehearse the letters in between attempts to recall them. (1)

   d) **i)** Effect of lack of rehearsal on memory

      ii) It leads to a decline in effectiveness of the encoding of memories.

      iii) Lack of rehearsal allows items in the STM to be displaced and forgotten before they can be encoded and stored in the LTM. (3)

7 See Figure An 18.1. (3)

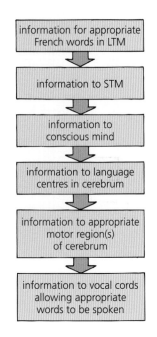

Figure An 18.1

8 **a)** attention

   b) groups

   c) repeating

   d) meaning

   e) visual, unusual

   f) overlearn

   g) short, long

   h) rest, recreation (10)

9 **a)** See core text pages 243–246. (6)

   b) See core text pages 245–246. (3)

Chapter 19   The cells of the nervous system and neurotransmitters at synapses

1 **a)** X = sensory neuron, Y = inter neuron, Z = motor neuron (3)

   b) Somatic, involuntary (2)

   c) Brain (1)

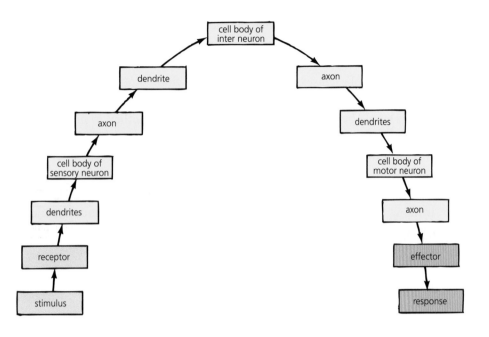

Figure An 19.1

2 See Figure An 19.1. (5)

3 E, B, C, F, D, A (1)

4 **a)** B

  b) D

  c) A

  d) C (3)

5 **a)** X = cone, Y = rod (2)

  b) 1 and 3 (1)

  c) Compared with cones, rods are much more sensitive to light and are able to transmit weak nerve impulses in dim light. Several of these impulses from convergently arranged rods are needed for the postsynaptic membrane to reach threshold. (3)

6 **a)** See core text pages 256–258. (5)

  b) See core text pages 261–262. (2)

  c) See core text page 260. (2)

7 **a)** **i)** 6

    ii) No

    iii) The error bars overlap. (3)

  b) **i)** 20

    ii) Yes

    iii) The error bars do not overlap. (3)

  c) A prolonged period of laughing can elevate the pain threshold. (1)

  d) Repeat the experiment but also take blood samples, before and after, from the members of both groups and analyse these for the presence of increased levels of endorphins. (2)

  e) Repeat the experiment with each person in isolation when viewing the video. (1)

8 **a)** **i)** X

    ii) Y (1)

  b) An agonist mimics a neurotransmitter and stimulates specific receptors to transmit nerve impulses. Drug X must be the agonist because an increase in its concentration brings about increased stimulation of receptors. An antagonist binds to specific receptors and blocks the action of the neurotransmitter. Drug Y must be the antagonist because an increase in its concentration brings about decreased stimulation of receptors. (2)

  c) **i)** 8

    ii) 8×10^{-9} (2)

  d) Drug Y is competing with the natural neurotransmitter for receptor sites on the postsynaptic membrane. But however high the concentration of drug Y, a few receptor sites will still become occupied by the natural neurotransmitter. (2)

9 **a)** P = 16.8; Q = 16.7 (2)

  b) **i)** It increased.

    ii) Because a higher frequency indicates that the

person took longer to appreciate the change in light and took longer to press the button. (3)

c) i) No

ii) Because only one member of each sex carried out the procedure. (2)

d) i) So that their systems would be completely clear of alcohol before the test began and therefore the only alcohol that could have any effect was the 80 mg consumed during the investigation.

ii) No eating or drinking for 3 hours before the test so that each subject would begin with an 'empty' stomach.
80 mg of alcohol given each time.
30-minute wait employed each time to allow absorption of alcohol to take place. (4)

e) i) Five trials were conducted for each condition.

ii) Many more subjects of both sexes should be used. The number of reaction time trials should be increased from five to ten. (3)

10 a) See core text page 268. (4)

b) See core text page 277. (5)

Chapter 20 Communication and social behaviour

1 a) As level of indiscriminate attachment decreases in intensity, level of specific attachment increases in intensity. (1)

b) i) 29–32 weeks

ii) Specific

iii) 0

iv) It makes the primary carer (e.g. mother) want to protect and take care of the child. (4)

2 The ones where the babies received little more than food and basic hygiene. Babies also need contact comfort to develop normally. (2)

3 a) i) Cloth = 18 hours; wire = 1 hour

ii) Infant monkeys spent more time in contact with the cloth 'mother'.

iii) No. The overall trend shown by the graph for groups A and B is the same. (3)

b) i) C

ii) They did not spend as much time with the cloth 'mother' compared with A and B. (2)

c) i) Wire

ii) It increased

iii) The fear score of an infant reared with the

wire 'mother' is much greater. Contact comfort reduces fear in infant monkeys. (3)

d) The interest level shown by infant monkeys for a cloth 'mother' is almost as high as that for live adult monkeys. The interest level shown for a wire 'mother' is almost as low as that for an empty room. (2)

4 a) A1 = 2, 4, 7, 11; A2 = 3, 5, 6, 10; P = 1, 5, 6, 8, 9, 10, 12 (6)

b) Because parents are not consistent and tend to vary their behaviour depending on their mood and circumstances. (1)

5 See Figure An 20.1. (7)

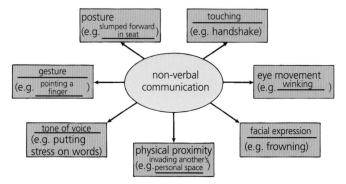

Figure An 20.1

6 a) This is more likely to make the potential customer warm to the sales assistant and believe what is being said. (1)

b) i) Smiling

ii) Speaking clearly and using a friendly tone of voice (3)

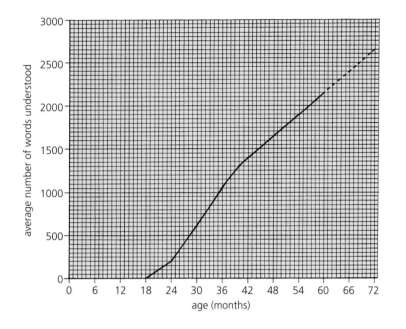

Figure An 20.2

7 **a)** See Figure An 20.2. (3)
  b) 41 months (1)
  c) 175% (1)
  d) A (1)
  e) 2650 (1)
8 **a) i)** Second 14
    ii) Second 10
    iii) It increased
    iv) It decreased (4)
  b) i) When listening, the person spends about 60% of the time gazing at the other person.
    ii) When speaking, the person spends about 40% of the time gazing at the other person. (2)
9 **a)** See core text pages 285–289. (5)
  b) See core text pages 289, 291. (4)
10 **a) i)** B
    ii) A (1)
  b) i) Distributed practice is more effective than massed practice.
    ii) It is thought that a motor memory is laid down by synaptic connections being formed between certain neurons following repetition of the skill. It is possible that more connections are formed during distributed practice spread over 20 days than during massed practice concentrated on the same day. (3)
  c) To increase the reliability of the results. (1)

  d) To prevent the introduction of a second variable factor. (1)
  e) The investigation could be repeated with a fresh set of volunteers exposed, this time, to an auditory distraction at each trial. The results would be compared with those for the version without the auditory distraction. (2)
11 **a)** Y. It is easier to learn a new skill by imitating an expert than by following a set of written instructions. (1)
  b) To prevent the introduction of a second variable factor. (1)
12 **a)** Behaviour that receives a **reward** regularly, undergoes **reinforcement**. In theory, therefore, behaviour that goes unrewarded should suffer **extinction** and disappear. (3)
  b) Giving him £1 sometimes would reinforce the bad behaviour intermittently and make it even more resistant to extinction. (2)
13 **a)** Learning curve (1)
  b) The larger the reward, the faster the learning process. (1)
  c) The rats have reached the best possible score and cannot improve. (1)
  d) Since there are only two choices available, the rats would score, on average, 50% correct responses even before learning the T-maze. (1)

e) To eliminate the possibility that the rats have some instinctive behaviour pattern that just happened to make them choose one side of the maze more frequently than the other. (1)

f) i) DE

ii) The food rewards were stopped.

iii)The size of the reward had no effect. (3)

14 a) i) Competing with others present resulted in a better performance.

ii) D (2)

b) i) Performance improves

ii) Performance remains unchanged

iii)During the repeat, the task is easier because it is more familiar. In group i) the competitors improve further because they are spurred on by the presence of one another. However this does not happen in group ii) because they are in isolation. (4)

15 **Deindividuation** is the loss by individuals of their personal identities. This behaviour is demonstrated by the members of the Ku Klux Klan who allow themselves to fall under the influence of **group pressure**. As part of a **faceless mob** enjoying complete **anonymity**, they feel confident enough to carry out disreputable deeds and indulge in a level of **risk-taking** that they would not consider doing on their own. (5)

16 This type of advertising tries to use identification to sell its product. The manufacturers of the product hope that potential customers will identify so closely with the gold medallist and his/her achievements and lifestyle that they will buy the endorsed product to be like their hero/heroine. (2)

17 a) See core text pages 299–300. (4)

b) See core text page 300. (3)

c) See core text page 301. (2)

Chapter 21 Non-specific defences

1 E, D, B, C, A (1)

2 a) i) White blood cell count

ii) Percentage

iii)Absolute refers to a value that is an actual number. Relative refers to a value that relates or compares two numbers. (3)

b) 1 microlitre (1×10^{-6} l) contains 200–600 cells. Therefore 1 litre contains 200–600 $\times 10^6$ cells = 2–6 $\times 10^8$ cells. (1)

c) i) Parasitic infection

ii) Rheumatoid arthritis and acute stress

iii)Neutrophil and lymphocyte (3)

d) See Figure An 21.1. (3)

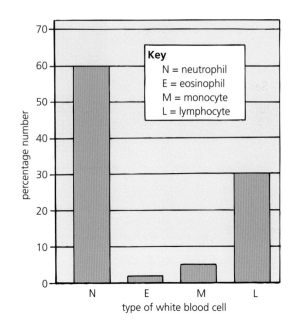

Figure An 21.1

3 a) i) Cascade

ii) Chemotaxis

iii)Osmosis

iv) Polysaccharide (4)

b) C5a (1)

c) See Figure An 21.2. (4)

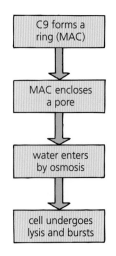

Figure An 21.2

d) 5000 times (1)

4 See core text pages 313–314. (9)

Chapter 22 Specific cellular defences

1 **a) i)** B

    ii) Non-self

    iii) Neither, nor

    iv) A, B, AB and O

    v) A, B, AB and O (5)

 b) See Table An 22.1. (8)

		Blood group of donor			
		A	B	AB	O
Blood group of recipient	A	–	+	+	–
	B	+	–	+	–
	AB	–	–	–	–
	O	+	+	+	–

(+ = agglutination; – = no agglutination)

Table An 22.1

 c) Q = A, R = O, S = AB, T = B (4)

2 **a) i)** First child = Dd, second = dd, third = Dd, fourth = dd

    ii) First child = Rh+, second = Rh–, third = Rh+, fourth = Rh– (4)

 b) i) Third child

    ii) Following the birth of the first child, the mother produced anti-D antibodies and is said to be sensitised. Therefore when she is carrying the third child, her anti-D antibodies will combine with the baby's antigens causing agglutination of many fetal red blood cells.

    iii) She could have been given anti-D immunoglobulins soon after the birth of the first Rh+ baby to destroy any D antigens before her immune system had time to respond.

    iv) The baby could be given a transfusion of blood. (6)

3 **a) i)** 8.8%

    ii) 12.4% (2)

 b) 1.5 (1)

 c) 3% (1)

 d) 16–24 (1)

 e) i) There are more male sufferers.

    ii) There are more female sufferers. (2)

 f) i) T

    ii) F, 7.4 and 15.4

    iii) F, 4.2 and 11.8

    iv) T

    v) T

    vi) F, 7.4 and 16.0 (6)

4 **a) and b)** See Figure An 22.1. (8)

5 1 = E, 2 = A, 3 = D, 4 = B, 5 = C (4)

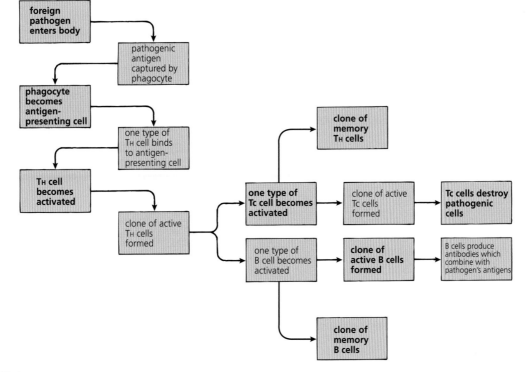

Figure An 22.1

Chapter 23   Transmission and control of infectious diseases

1 a) A = food, B = hygiene, C = faeces, D = cross-infection, E = poultry, F = pigeons (5)
   b) Cook food thoroughly.
       Practise good hygiene such as washing hands before handling food.
       Prevent flies gaining access to food. (3)
2   1 = C, 2 = E, 3 = A, 4 = B, 5 = D (4)
3   See core text pages 333–335. (9)

Chapter 24   Active immunisation and vaccination and the evasion of specific immune response by pathogens

1 a) Phase I used a few, paid, healthy people whereas phase II used many, unpaid, asthma sufferers. (3)
   b) So that any improvements in sufferers receiving Q can be attributed to Q if the same improvements are absent from the control group. (2)
   c) The results of phase III showed that patients on Q suffered fewer asthma attacks and used their inhalers less often than the control group. (2)
   d) i) An inactive copy of the drug
      ii) They had gained a psychological benefit from taking the placebo or their condition had just happened to improve. (2)
   e) i) Addition
      ii) Although the condition of many sufferers improved, less than half were able to give up inhaled steroids. (2)
   f) On average, elderly people's health is poorer than that of young people so a new drug might affect them adversely. Elderly people use so many medicines that the data produced would be unreliable. (2)
2 a) P and N (1)
   b) A and P (1)
   c) A and N (1)
3 a) i) 4
      ii) 3 (2)
   b) Diphtheria, tetanus and polio (1)
   c) Measles, mumps and rubella (1)
4 a) i) Diphtheria
      ii) Tuberculosis (2)
   b) Good food and improved quality of housing. (2)
   c) i) 4
      ii) 60%

iii) 1882
iv) 0.8 (4)
   d) People sleeping 'rough' in cold, damp conditions become susceptible to respiratory infections including tuberculosis because their resistance is low. (1)
5 a) i) Y
      ii) X
      iii) Vaccination began earlier and eradication was achieved earlier in X. (2)
   b) This is supported by the fact that the start of the vaccination campaign was followed each time by an apparent surge in cases when in fact this high level probably existed all along. It is hardly likely that it was caused by vaccination. (2)
   c) i) Almost complete eradication of the disease.
      ii) Many strains of the pathogen exist and it is able to change the antigenic proteins present on its surface. (2)
6 a) i) 1 week
      ii) 450 (2)
   b) i) 10
      ii) Week 27–28
      iii) Antigenic variation (3)
   c) i) Early
      ii) The number of trypanosomes dropped during the first half of the week. (2)
7 a) Antigenic drift results from mutations that occur naturally and continuously. Antigenic shift results from the occasional combination of genetic material from two different viral strains forming a new strain. (2)
   b) A new influenza **vaccine** is needed every year because all the strains of the **virus** are continuously undergoing genetic **drift** as a result of **mutation**. Therefore one or more **new** strains appear each year able to resist **antibodies** that blocked the **infection** by the **previous** viral strain. (4)
   c) C (1)
   d) Antigenic drift results from natural mutations and these affect the genetic material of all organisms including influenza viruses A, B and C. Antigenic shift involves the combination of genetic material from two (or more) strains of the same virus from different hosts. Unlike B and C, influenza virus A can infect both humans and birds and therefore opportunities arise for

antigenic shift to occur when two different strains of type A virus meet. (2)

e) See Figure An 24.1. (3)

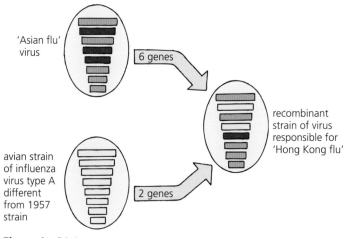

Figure An 24.1

8 See core text pages 343–346. (9)